VIEWS ON GENERAL SYSTEMS THEORY

PUBLICATIONS FROM THE SYSTEMS RESEARCH CENTER,

CASE INSTITUTE OF TECHNOLOGY

Ellis A. Johnson, Director

VIEWS ON GENERAL SYSTEMS THEORY
edited by Mihajlo D. Mesarović

SYSTEMS: RESEARCH AND DESIGN
edited by Donald P. Eckman

VIEWS ON GENERAL SYSTEMS THEORY

proceedings of The Second Systems
Symposium at Case Institute
of Technology

edited by
MIHAJLO D. MESAROVIĆ

Associate Professor of Engineering
Systems Research Center
Case Institute of Technology

John Wiley & Sons, Inc., New York · London · Sydney

CONTRIBUTORS

Russell L. Ackoff
Professor of Operations Research, Case Institute of Technology, Cleveland, Ohio

W. Ross Ashby
Professor of Electrical Engineering, University of Illinois, Urbana, Illinois

Kenneth E. Boulding
Professor of Economics, University of Michigan, Ann Arbor, Michigan

Abraham Charnes
Research Professor of Applied Mathematics and Economics, Northwestern University, Evanston, Illinois

C. West Churchman
Professor of Business Administration, University of California, Berkeley, California

William W. Cooper
Professor of Economics and Industrial Administration, Carnegie Institute of Technology, Schenley Park, Pittsburgh 13, Pennsylvania

Rudolf F. Drenick
Professor of Engineering, Polytechnic Institute of Brooklyn, Brooklyn, New York

R. W. Gerard
Professor of Biological Sciences, University of California, Irvine, California

Robert Kalaba
Staff Mathematician, The RAND Corporation, Santa Monica, California

William K. Linvill
Professor of Engineering, Stanford University, Stanford, California

Mihajlo D. Mesarović
Associate Professor of Engineering, Case Institute of Technology, Cleveland 6, Ohio

John Myhill

Professor of Philosophy, Institute for Advanced Study, Princeton, New Jersey

Hilary Putnam

Professor of the Philosophy of Science, Massachusetts Institute of Technology, Cambridge, Massachusetts

Anatol Rapoport

Professor of Mathematical of Biology, University of Michigan, Ann Arbor, Michigan

Lotfi A. Zadeh

Professor of Electrical Engineering, University of California, Berkeley, California

Dedicated to the Memory of
Professor Donald P. Eckman
1915–1962
Founder and First Director
of the Systems Research Center

FOREWORD*

It is a great pleasure to have this opportunity to meet the participants of the Second Systems Symposium. A number of you also took part in the first conference held two years ago. In the intervening years the development of a logical framework for the design of large and complex systems has become of ever more pressing urgency.

One of the complicating problems is the lack of public understanding of the meaning of the term "system," as we use it, and of the goals of systems research. The term is widely used by all segments of the population, but its meaning is clouded.

As a result, a request for support of a systems research project brings diverse reactions.

Yet one thing seems to be very much in our favor. There is general agreement that the most crucial problems our society faces involve large and complex systems.

We cannot ignore these problems in the hope that they will go away, or choose from those confronting us the ones that are simplest or easiest to solve. It is true that a chemical company can choose not to develop a new process, but the alternative may be failure to keep abreast of competition resulting in the eventual decline of the business. A nation may elect not to create a defense system or modify its economic system to meet the competitive pressures of the modern world, but again, the alternative may be disaster.

Strong arguments for serious and large-scale efforts on many fronts to develop a logical framework for the design of complicated systems can be made, and there is clear and ample evidence to support the thesis that better solutions to some of these large-scale systems problems can now be found.

It is clear that the problem is interdisciplinary in character. Therefore the solution cannot be sought and found within the scope of any one traditional area of activity but requires the contributions and cooperation of all concerned.

* At the banquet, Second Systems Symposium, April 1963.

It is obvious that the most powerful available mathematical tools are essential, and that many of the problems are so complex that large computing machines have to be used. Wherever possible, dynamic measurements must be made under actual operating conditions and used to help develop general theoretical formulations.

In man-machine systems, biological understanding at both the micro and macro levels is essential. I am speaking of a man-machine system in which man or a subsystem of man appears as a component of the system. There are systems problems, again man-machine problems, where men appear in groups in the system. In this kind of system, no logical framework of design can be formulated without a deeper understanding than we now have of group dynamics, of relations between groups, and of relations between individuals and groups.

The idea that it is possible to deal with integrated and intricate man-machine systems through a general systems theory is interesting enough to attract this distinguished group of conference participants, but we must not forget our limitations. We still await a Clerk Maxwell to provide a complete and unifying theory; and if we are overzealous and attempt to expand our definition of a general systems theory to include the interrelation of all things, I do not believe we will achieve our goal. However, I believe we can achieve a framework of logic which will enable us to design and predict systems of far greater complexity than those which can be dealt with today.

I do not believe that this goal can be achieved by limited sorties at the existing front of knowledge. I am inclined to think that the time has come to take bold action and risk landings well beyond the existing frontier. The risk of such landings may be great, but the possible rewards justify the risk.

Despite the sobering nature of these problems, a complex sociological-economic-engineering system, such as the predicted Great Lakes megalopolis which may develop through the merging of existing cities in the region as our population grows, offers challenging experimental possibilities. The introduction of planned and monitored diversity offers an exciting alternative to the more self-contained experiments of the controllable university research laboratory.

The image of our subject that I have, then, is that general systems theory will be used as one of the major tools guiding the design of large interdisciplinary systems. Furthermore, such theory must itself be developed with interdisciplinary support rather than solely by a special group of new general systems theorists. The over-all cooperation needed to insure the success of systems research will involve an interdisciplinary research team; participation and exchange of faculty between several institutions; support by a number of sponsors, each interested in some particular aspect or subsystem of the over-all systems problem; and a broader experimental base. The result of such a deliberately designed three-dimensional disciplinary-research agency-sponsored matrix might well have a revolutionary impact not only on the rate of progress in systems research but also on the affairs of man.

JOHN HRONES
Vice President of Academic Affairs
Case Institute of Technology

Cleveland, Ohio
February 1964

PREFACE

The last decade has witnessed a renewal of a strong interest among scientists and engineers in a better understanding of the basic theoretical concepts used in the various disciplines. Questions have been raised as to whether the similarities among the basic concepts are sufficient to justify development of a more general theory which will represent a basis for the more specialized theories. The essential idea for such an undertaking is very appealing in its simplicity. Knowledge in any particular discipline is embodied in a theory which as such is an abstract construct. It is only natural to expect that many of these constructs have strong similarities or, perhaps, are essentially the same. It is, of course, quite another matter actually to find these similarities as well as new concepts which will bring diverse developments together. What might be the road leading toward such a development, and what are the prospects for its success, was the theme of the Second Systems Symposium held at Case Institute of Technology in the spring of 1963.

It has been pointed out in several circles that the starting point for a general theory can be found in the notion of a system or, rather, a general system. The theory then becomes general systems theory. I will not venture here to elaborate on the meaning of such a theory. After all, this is the subject of all the contributions in this volume. Let me only very briefly emphasize the motivation for developing such a theory. Recently, it was very pointedly emphasized by Dr. Simon Ramo that the human community is in a race: "Systems engineering versus the rapidly increasing complexity of our growing technological civilization." Systems engineering should offer some facilities to understand, and to control such complexities. In a broader context, the ever increasing complexity of the world we live in requires that our understanding of this phenomenon be based on a broader theoretical basis.

The motivation for an attempt to develop such a theory is therefore both scientific, with the objective of improving our understanding of the natural and social phenomena, and practical (engineering), with the objective to provide better methods for the synthesis and control of complex systems.

The idea of developing a general theory that would provide a more unified picture of our experience is not a new one. Actually, this idea has been very much cherished by classical thinkers and philosophers and has been revived occasionally throughout history. What characterizes the present attempt toward such a theory, however, is its concern with scientific rather than philosophical matters which, actually, are being developed by scientists and engineers. The interest in the theory arises from the needs of the practicing scientist and engineer rather than from scientific or philosophical curiosity. However, this is not to imply that the theory might not have philosophical implications.

The contributions comprising this book represent slightly revised versions of the talks delivered at the Second Systems Symposium. At the time when the symposium was held, the objective of the symposium was stated to be the clarification of the following problems:

1. Basic characteristics of general systems theory.
2. Review of major developments achieved to date.
3. Statement of current problems of importance.
4. Prospect for the future.

Seventeen speakers participated in the formal presentation and panel discussion, and more than 200 attendants engaged in active discussion during the two days of the conference. At the time when the book was scheduled to go into print, 14 manuscripts had reached the editor.

The manuscripts represent rather successfully the spectrum of opinions expressed at the conference. All contributors agreed on one point—necessity for the development of a general systems theory. However, opinions widely differed regarding the type of the theory and the direction in which it should be developed. To appreciate all the nuances, it is certainly advisable to go through all the contributions. However, the editor had the task of trying to indicate the relations and diversities that appeared in the discussion. In this particular instance the editor's job was made more complex by the fact that he took an active part in the discussion and provided a contribution to the proceedings. I will restrict my comments, therefore, to the approach taken toward the problem of how to develop the general systems theory.

First of all, some of the participants took a definite stand, venturing to define a system and then discussing the consequences of such a definition. A second group of participants argued that the general systems theory should not be formalized since this very act will limit its generating power and make it more or less specific. A third group proposed to consider systems theory as a viewpoint taken when one approaches the solution of a given (practical) problem. Finally, it was expressed that a broad-enough collection of powerful methods for the synthesis (design) of systems of diverse kinds should be considered as constituting the sought-for theory and any further integration was unnecessary. There were also participants that shared the viewpoints of more than one of the above groups.

It is not apparent which of the viewpoints will prevail. It might very well happen that several developments along different lines will take place. At any rate, it is believed that diverse viewpoints are presented in the 14 contributions and, as such, they can present the cornerstone for further developments of the general systems theory in whatever direction appears to be promising.

Many persons have contributed their time and effort to make the Second Systems Symposium possible. Dr. Simon Ramo, an old supporter and friend of the Systems Research Center, has helped with the solution of the financial problems in connection with the conference. Dr. John Hrones, Vice-President of Case Institute, again has helped the Systems Research Center with the organizational problem as he has done so many times in the past. Dr. Raymond Nelson, Director of the Computing Center at Case Institute, was acting-director at the Systems Center at the time of the organization of the conference and his enthusiastic backing of the project made it a success. Dr. Ellis Johnson, present Director of the Systems Center, continued to support the project in the same spirit until its final completion. Dr. Ray Bolz, Head of the Engineering Division at Case, served as the chairman of the session at the symposium. He has always been instrumental in stimulating the systems activities in the Engineering Division.

The reader of the book should join the editor in acknowledgment of the help of Dr. Lester Goodman, Assistant Director of the Systems Research Center, who served as cochairman of the conference. The research on present system theory in the Systems Research Center has been supported by ONR under Contract 1141 (12). The results of this research are reported in the Case contribution to this book. In particular, Mr. R. Wilcox and Dr. M. Shelly of that office encouraged development of that contribution through repeated visits to Case and discussions on the subject.

Finally a word seems appropriate regarding the arrangement and sequence of the chapters. Since all the contributions represent, in essence, independent viewpoints, no grouping or proper sequencing of the chapters was attempted. Rather it was decided to put them in order of their presentation at the conference. The reader can start with any chapter he chooses without any loss of continuity.

While listening to the presentations, Professor Boulding was inspired to write small poems about some of the contributions. We decided to include them, hoping that they might enlighten the reading and, in themselves, present some kind of bridge between two cultures.

MIHAJLO D. MESAROVIĆ

Cleveland, Ohio
February 1964

CONTENTS

CHAPTER 1

FOUNDATIONS FOR A GENERAL SYSTEMS THEORY

MIHAJLO D. MESAROVIĆ

According to Mesarović
A set of proper statements which
Has mastered, in well-ordered schools
A set of transformation rules
Which rules in turn have rules to twist 'em
Deserves the name of general system.

All systems, it is now proposed
Are either open, or are closed,
The closed have one-to-one relations
But don't result in innovations.
The open are disturbed, adaptive
Or Heisenberg-observer-captive.

K. B.

INTRODUCTION

Since the very beginning of scientific inquiry, emphasis has alternated between the particular (data and facts) and the general (similarities and theories). Theory requires the facts on which to build, and facts and evidences need theory for understanding of the phenomena. Traditionally, theories have been developed within the boundaries of a particular field; i.e., they have been concerned with a given class of real systems such as biological, physical, chemical, etc. Rapid advances in the collection of data, as well as the development of theories within particular fields of scientific inquiry, have created a new problem on a higher level. Namely, a need appeared for a general theory which would serve as a foundation for other specific theories, crossing the boundaries of the different fields, and ultimately resulting in a deeper understanding of the world we live in.

In addition to the scientific interest, the solution of certain very practical problems appears to require the help of such a general theory;

hence development of this theory has become a matter of paramount importance. For example, in engineering (taken in a very broad sense), a general theory that crosses traditional fields appears necessary for the design of systems that include men, computers, and machines. Similarly, in the sciences, the proper understanding of certain phenomena, or certain real systems, requires their observation in the broader context of larger systems which now include the systems studied traditionally by the different fields.

In this chapter, a definite attempt is made to lay down the foundation for the development of such a general theory. Before elaborating further, the basic motivation and justification for the selection of a theory of this type are discussed. Only the basic concepts of the theory are outlined here because of space limitations. Sufficient details are presented, however, to indicate the approach taken. A fuller account of the theory will be presented in a forthcoming book.[11]

MOTIVATION

As mentioned in the foregoing section, both scientific and technological advances exhibit a need for a general theory. Let us consider the motivations for such a theory.

A basic methodological tool used in the development of scientific theories is the method of analogy. It suffices here to discuss this method informally. In essence, the method of analogy has the following underlining philosophy: An equivalence relation is established between two systems (either of the systems may be real or conceptual). The equivalence relation indicates that aspects of the behavior of the two systems which are the same. One can then make certain inferences about the behavior (or perhaps some relevant aspect of it) of one system from the study and observation of the other. The selection of the system to be studied is based on practical consideration; namely, the system on which the observations are to be made is selected so as to be simpler than the actual system in all respects not related by the established equivalence. The system used in the investigation is then called a model.

It is interesting to note that in science and in mathematics somewhat opposite directions are followed in the selection of a model. In the sciences, the model is invariably an abstract, mathematical system, or a much simpler physical system than the original. In mathematics, however, a model is a more specific and less abstract analogy of the actual system. In the theory proposed here the model can be understood in either sense.

Since the theory of any specific scientific field depends on analogies, it seems reasonable that the general theory should similarly rely on a general type of analogy. Also, the models used in the general theory should be of a general kind.

We turn now to engineering. The building of complex systems, particularly those involving men, posed new problems which could not be solved with the traditional tools and techniques. A new field consequently developed under the name of Systems Engineering. So far it has relied, to a large extent, on the tools and techniques of other fields, combined with the practitioner's experience and intuition. The principal reason for this was a lack of theoretical foundations from which methodological procedures could be derived. One of the objectives of general systems theory is to provide such a foundation.

REQUIREMENTS

We consider now the basic requirements that a general theory should satisfy in the light of the motivations discussed in the foregoing section. The following two appear to be among the most important.

1. The general theory should be general enough to encompass different types of already existing specific theories. It should, therefore, be sufficiently abstract so that its terms and concepts are relevant to specialized theories. Clearly, the more abstract statements have a broader context but, at the same time, they carry less information regarding the behavior of any particular system. The general concepts must emphasize the common features of all the systems considered yet neglect the specific aspects of the behavior of any particular system. The real challenge in developing a general theory is, therefore, to find the proper level of abstraction. The concepts must have wide application, while the conclusions which they lead to must provide sufficient information for proper understanding of the particular class of phenomena under consideration.

2. The general theory has to have a scientific character in the sense that its concepts and terms must be uniquely defined within the proper context. If the general theory is to be of any help in solving scientific and engineering problems, it must not rely on vague, ill-defined, almost poetic analogies. The basis for the general theory must be solid so

that its conclusions have practical meaning for real systems. Reliance on vague analogies is the main weakness of the general theories previously conceived. Let us hasten, however, to add that by requiring scientific status for the general theory we do not want to imply that it should somehow consist of the set of dogmas revealing the essential truth of the real phenomena. On the contrary it is to be expected that a general theory, much as other human intellectual innovations, will age, be updated and rejuvenated. However, at any given time, within the framework of existing knowledge, the general theory should be designed on solid foundations.

In the following sections a general theory will be proposed which is abstract enough yet definite enough to be useful. In the spirit of the remarks in this section, however, none of the basic concepts of the theory should be considered as unalterable. Only the type of the proposed theory and its spirit are to be considered as invariant.

BASIC CHARACTERISTICS OF THE THEORY

The general theory proposed here has the following basic characteristics:

1. It is developed around the notion of a system. Since it can be argued that both science and engineering are concerned with the study of real systems and their behavior, it follows that a general theory should be concerned with the study of the general systems. In the next section, the concepts of general systems will be introduced on a technical basis. It suffices for the present discussion to consider a general system as an abstract analog or model of a class of real systems. General systems theory is then a theory of general models. It might be argued that a general theory should be broader than the concept of systems, but, in order to preserve the definite character of the theory as discussed in the foregoing section, it appears to be of considerable advantage to base the theory on the concept of a system.

2. General systems theory, as a theory of general models, must encompass the specific theories concerned with the more restrictive types of models; e.g., the theory of linear systems, the theory of Markov systems, etc. These theories can be regarded as being concerned with the specific types of models. The delineation between general systems theory and the theory of specific systems is very difficult and often rather arbitrary. This is, however, as it should be since, in principle, there is nothing to be gained from constructing sharp boundaries

among the fields. Flexibility in this respect will only help further development and growth. However, this should not be confused with the requirements for solid foundations as argued in the last section. No matter how we delineate the field, the basic concepts and notions must be consistent with the context proposed.

3. General systems theory also unifies the theories of different aspects of systems behavior such as communication, control, adaptation, learning self-organization, theory of computing and algorithms, etc. This unification is, of course, on a more abstract level. It also helps someone interested in a specific aspect of the systems behavior to understand this in a broader context.

4. General systems theory in its development uses largely more abstract branches of mathematics and in this sense is related to the mathematical theory of formal systems. However, the meaning of the terms used is of primary importance to general systems theory while it is largely immaterial for formal mathematics. This becomes especially clear when discussing the goal-seeking behavior of general systems. For example, from a general systems viewpoint, the solution of an equation might be important only insofar as it reveals the behavior of the system under consideration.

5. We are now in a position to outline more clearly the objectives and scope of general systems theory and to consider the basic methodology used. General systems theory is a scientific undertaking concerned with the study of the behavior of general systems. Its methodology is essentially scientific in nature. The relation between the investigator and the system under study is analogous to the relation between nature and the natural scientist. Namely, a general system is given either in terms of mathematical equations or computer specifications, or a physical analog, or a verbal description, etc., and the objective is to discover the basic properties of its behavior.

CONCEPT OF A GENERAL SYSTEM

The problem of selecting the proper level of generality for the basis of general systems theory is indeed formidable. We shall somewhat circumvent this problem, in this section, by introducing the concept of a system in the most general context while using more specific types of systems in the development of the theory.

The concept of the general system introduced in this section is instructive since it indicates how one can discuss the behavior of a real system by using only linguistic constructions while simultaneously satisfying the requirements of a definite basis, as discussed in the foregoing section.

Three different definitions of a general system are introduced, but all three will be on the same level of abstraction.

The first and most general approach is to use a linguistic definition for a general system. To arrive at this concept of a general system, several preliminary concepts must first be introduced.

One starts with the concept of a formal statement in a language L. The language under consideration may be a natural language as, e.g., English, a computer language, or any formal language generated in a recursive manner by a machine. A *formal statement* F in a language L is defined as a sentence which is formed according to the rules of grammar of the respective language but the truth of which is not revealed by the statement itself. It is assumed that the formal statement has some unspecified constituents and, consequently, the formal statement might be taken to be true for some values of these constituents.

Assume that a set of formal statements K is given. If a subset M of these statements is taken to be true, it defines a *theory* T *over* K. Namely, theory T conjectures that only the statements in subset M are true, the remaining statements being left unspecified.

Assume now that the formal statements in M are such that the unspecified constituents represent formal objects. Formal statements are then called *proper statements*. We have then:

Linguistic Definition: A general system is a set of proper statements.

The second approach is based on set-theoretic considerations. Formal objects are defined explicitly rather than as conceptual classes via formal statements. (Conceptual class is understood in the sense of Curry.[2]) One starts by defining a family of sets $X_1 \cdots, X_n$. Each set specifies a formal object. Namely, the formal object defined by the set X_j can take on the form of any of the elements of the set X_j. The elements of X_j can be called values of the object in X_j. The cartesian product X of the family of sets is then formed

$$X = X_1 * X_2 * X_3 * \cdots * X_n \tag{1}$$

We can now introduce the following:

Explicit Definition: A general system is a proper subset of X.

$$X_s \subset X \tag{2}$$

Actually, a proper subset of the cartesian set X defines a relation among the objects $X_1, \cdots, X_n$. Notice that an element of the set X_j

can itself be a set, e.g., in the case of dynamic systems. The elements of sets X_j are then time functions defined on appropriate intervals (t_1, t_2) and, therefore, they represent the infinite set of values which the time functions will take in that interval.

The explicit definition can be also stated in the following way:

A general system is a relation defined on the cartesian product X.

A general system is therefore specified by

$$X = X_1 * \cdots * X_n \quad \text{and} \quad R = \{R_1, \cdots, R_j\} \tag{3}$$

The difficulties in the linguistic as well as in the explicit specification of a general system lie in the fact that both X and R can be infinite sets which can be specified only as inductive classes, i.e., by defining effective processes which would generate them. The introduction of such generating processes leads to the implicit definition of a general system.

First, a systems term set X_j is specified by an effective process using the following prerequisites:

1. Set of initial elements.
2. Effective procedure for generating new elements of X_j from initial or previously generated elements.
3. Closure condition which requires that only elements generated by (1) and (2) are elements of X_j.

Second, systems relations R are also specified inductively in the following way:
1. A set of relations T is given:

$$T = \{T_1, \cdots, T_i\} \tag{4}$$

2. Any of the systems relations R_j is represented as a sequence of relations from the set T.

$$R_j = \{T_{j_1}, T_{j_2}, \cdots, T_{jm_j}\} \tag{5}$$

3. A set of rules of combination, $P = \{P_1, \cdots, P_n\}$, is given which specifies how the sequences $R_j = \{T_1, \cdots, T_{jm_j}\}$ are formed.

We can now introduce the following:

Implicit (Syntactic) Definition: A general system is defined by:

1. A set of implicitly defined formal objects.
2. A set of elementary transformations T.
3. A set of rules P for forming the sequences of T.
4. A set of statements indicating initial forms of the formal objects for use in generating new forms of the objects.

Notice that in the context of the linguistic approach items 1 through 3 define the class of formal statements and that only item 4 makes possible the formulation of a theory of formal objects, i.e., a general system.

OPEN AND CLOSED SYSTEMS

Consider an explicitly defined system. The subset X_s is essentially a set of n tuples. A given n tuple, element of X_s, will be called an exemplar. The elements of these n tuples consist of all admissible values for the formal objects. We now define a class of systems $X_s{}^1$, $X_s{}^2$, $\cdots$, $X_s{}^m$ such that $X_s{}^j \subset X_s$ for all j's.

A problem of primary importance in the application of systems theory to real systems is related to the existence of effective means to distinguish among the systems $X_s{}^1$, $\cdots$, $X_s{}^m$. Assume that an exemplar $x_i \in X_s$ is given. An equivalence relation, $L_1(x_i, X_s)$, defined on X_s will permit the determination of a proper subset $X_{si}(L_1) \subset X_s$ which contains the given exemplar $x_i \in X_{si}(L_1)$. At the same time, the relation L_1 determines which of the systems $X_s{}^1$, $\cdots$, $X_s{}^m$ are under consideration, since only those systems that contain $X_{si}(L_1)$ are considered as being relevant. Assume now that a finite sequence of equivalence relations $L_1, \cdots, L_n$ exists, so that the set $X_{si}(L_1, \cdots, L_n)$ consists of a single element. In other words, by applying the sequence of equivalence relations $L_1, \cdots, L_n$, the exemplar x_i will be uniquely determined since it will be the only element in the set $X_{si}(L_1, \cdots, L_n)$. Such a sequence of relations is called an *effective identification process*. We can now introduce the following concept:

A general system $X_s{}^j$ is termed closed if and only if for every $x_i \in X_s{}^j$ there exists an effective identification process.

By using appropriate effective processes it is possible to distinguish a closed system $X_s{}^j$ from any other system $X_s{}^i \subset X_s$. The existence of an effective process is not a property of a general system but rather the result of the observer's relation with the system itself. An equivalence relation L_j can be considered as a measurement while an effective process (i.e., a sequence of relations $L_1, \cdots, L_n$) can be considered as an experiment performed on a real system.

A system for which the conditions outlined above are not satisfied, i.e., *for which there is at least one $x_i \in X_s{}^k$ for which an effective identification process does not exist, is called an open system.*

In essence, if a system is open, it cannot be distinguished from some other system $X_s{}^i$. In general, a system becomes open if in the hypothesis we are able to make about the system (and which we test by the experiments), some of the principal constituents are omitted, e.g., a smaller number of formal objects is assumed.

Three typical cases of open systems are:

1. A system which is not completely isolated from its environment (the system has "disturbances" or uncertainties).

2. A system which responds to the experimentation in such a way as to cause permanent changes in its behavior (adaptive or self-organizing systems).

3. A system with which the experimenter is interacting; i.e., while influencing the system he is, at the same time, influenced by it. (The experimenter is "inside" rather than "outside" of the system during experimentation.)

In dealing with an open system, one is confronted with a completely different situation than when dealing with a closed system. Most of the conceptual difficulties in decision making and control problems arise from the fact that the system under consideration is open and decision has to be made in the presence of uncertainties. The fact that some real systems result only in open general systems is of primary epistemological importance.

STRUCTURE

The concept of the structure of a system is very important but has, as yet, received very little attention. In this section we introduce the concept of the structure of a general system and show how it can be used in the theory of implicitly defined systems.

Consider an explicitly defined system. In general, the relation R has at least one constant constituent which has a specific value. Thus, R can be considered as a specific example of a more abstract relation which can be obtained when the given constituent is left unspecified. For example in the formal statement, "He is older than Jack," the systems relation is, "older than." However, it can be considered as a special instant of the relation,

$$\text{"is (of different age) than"}$$

or, equivalently,

$$\text{"is } \genfrac{}{}{0pt}{}{(\text{older})}{(\text{younger})} \text{ than"}$$

In the relations used in analysis, the unspecified constituents usually range over a set of numbers or functions (often time functions).

The system relation R can be considered as being defined by an abstract relation and the specific values of the unspecified constituents, so-called relational constituents;

$$R = \{T, \zeta\} \tag{6}$$

where T = systems structure,

ζ = set of relationed constituents.

We now have the following definition:

The structure of a system is obtained by abstracting the system relation, i.e., by leaving unspecified all the relational constituents.

An interesting example of how to derive a system structure is offered by the case of linear dynamic systems.[13] Consider a single variable linear system described by

$$y(t) = \int_{-\infty}^{t} F(\tau)\, x(t - \tau)\, d\tau \tag{7}$$

or

$$yRx$$

The systems relation can be represented in at least two ways: First, by taking time function $F(\tau)$ as the constituent so that the systems relation is

$$R = \{C, F(\tau)\} \tag{8}$$

where C is the algebraic operation of convolution. The system structure is then given by the operation C; $T = C$; $\zeta = F(\tau)$. Second, the systems structure can be obtained by abstracting certain numerical parameters associated with the time function $F(\tau)$. For example, for the first-order differential system the relation becomes

$$R = \left\{ \frac{1}{s}, \,\cdot\,, +, \theta, K \right\} \tag{9}$$

where $1/s$, $\cdot$, and $+$ are operations of integration, multiplication, and addition respectively, and constituents θ and K are parameters of the system called the time constant and gain respectively. Systems structure is then $T = \{1/s, \cdot, +\}$ and the relational constituents are $\zeta = \{\theta, K\}$.

Recognition of a systems structure involves imbedding the systems relation into a set of relations differing only in the values for some constituents. If this set of relations is not explicitly given, one can apparently select many different sets in which the system relations can be imbedded. The selection of the set T is then a matter of practical concern. For example, if one is concerned with modifying the system so as to improve its behavior, the systems relation should be imbedded in such a set that the selection of the relations can be accomplished by selecting the value for the unspecified constituent. Such a selection can be made in an organized manner, e.g., by using some method of optimization. However, selection of the structure itself, i.e., the set of relations, remains in the domain of a heuristic decision.

In the process of so-called systems identification, it is of primary importance to distinguish between the identification of the system structure and the identification of the system relations. Briefly, the problem of identification is the following: Given a set of input-output pairs, find the system relation. The solution of the identification problem consists essentially of two steps: (1) the selection of the system's structure T and (2) matching of the system's behavior with the relations in the set T in order to find the best values for the relational constituents ζ.

The second step can be undertaken systematically, but it is very important to emphasize that it must always be preceded by the first step which, in general, is based on guesses or experience. For example, in the case of a dynamic system, the assumption that the system is linear is equivalent to the selection of the convolution operation for the system's structure. The identification problem consists then of selecting the time function $F(\tau)$ in the best possible way.

Let us now show how the structure of an implicitly defined system can be found. As an appropriate representative of this class of systems, consider an elementary formal system (EFS) defined by Smullyan by the following items: [10]

1. An inductively defined class of finite sequences of strings which are well-formed formulas defined on the three alphabets—for symbols, for variables, and for predicates.

2. Two binary operations—R_1 for substitution, and R_2 for modus ponens.

3. A closure condition specifying that only elements obtained by repeated application of 2 on 1 are admissible systems terms.

To find the structure of the EFS, we must exhibit its explicit definition. Two new concepts must be introduced:

1. A set of designation signs θ and ζ

$$\theta = \{\tau_1, \cdots, \tau_j, \cdots\} \quad \text{and} \quad \zeta = \{\zeta_1, \zeta_2\} \tag{10}$$

θ is the set of designation signs associated with well-formed formulas while ζ is the set of signs associated with each of the relations R_1 and R_2.

2. A new binary operation $z = M_j[y_j, \tau_j]$ defined in the following way:

$$(a)\ (\tau \neq \tau_j)\ \rightarrow\ (z = 0)$$
$$(b)\ (\tau = \tau_j)\ \rightarrow\ (z = y_j) \tag{11}$$

where y_j is the result of the application of the relations R_1 or R_2 at time $t = t_j$. Relation M_j is essentially a storing operation active if $\tau = \tau_j$.

We can now introduce an explicit definition of the EFS, which we denote as MEFS, by specifying:

A. An inductively defined class of well-formed formulas.

B. A set E having triplets of the designation signs as elements,

$$E = \{e_j\}; e_j = \langle \mu_j^1, \zeta_j, \mu_j^2 \rangle \tag{12}$$

where μ_j^1 is either a designation sign τ_i or a well-formed formula; μ_j^2 has the same interpretation as μ_j^1; ζ is either ζ_1 or ζ_2.

C. Two triadic relations R_1 and R_2 and a set of binary operations $\{M_j\}$.

D. A closure condition.

The diagram of the system is given in Fig. 1. The designation triplets of the input at any given time determine both the relation and the formula on which the selected relation R_1 or R_2 will be applied. The result is "stored" by the relation M_j. By applying the appropriate sequence of designation triplets at the input, the systems theorems are generated at the output.

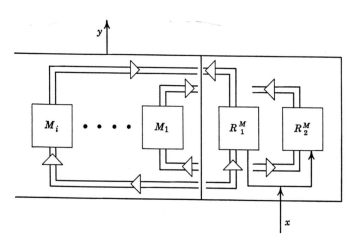

FIG. 1. MEFS system, $x = \{x_i\} = \{\langle \tau_i, \zeta_i, \tau_i^2 \rangle\}$. $y =$ output.

The structure of MEFS is now specified by the following set of relations:

$$T = \{R_1, R_2, M_1, M_2, \cdots, M_n, \cdots\} \tag{13}$$

where T, in general, is an infinite set.

Since EFS and MEFS are equivalent in the sense that both generate the same set of theorems, T can be considered as the structure of EFS.

The explicit definition of the system depends upon the type of the new relation M. It is possible to derive the structure of the EFS by using different relations $M_j{}^1$

$$z_j = M_j{}^1(x_j) \tag{14}$$

where $M_j{}^1$ is defined in the following way: $z_j(t_j) = x(t_j - T_j)$; i.e., the output of $M_j{}^1$ is the input delayed by T_j seconds. This representation indicates the dynamic behavior of the system, but the programming of the input sequences of designation signs is much more complex.

The introduction of the concept of structure in the study of formal systems permits an approach to decidability problems from the viewpoint of reproducibility discussed in the next section. Also, a systems interpretation of the Gödel incompleteness theorems is possible. However, these problems are technically too complex to be dealt with herein.

DECOMPOSITION AND STATE OF THE SYSTEM

An important (practical) problem concerns the possibility of decomposing or reticulating systems into subsystems. It is of interest to learn what can be said about this matter on the level of our present general discussion. Let us first introduce the concept of decomposition. Assume a system specified explicitly by a polyadic nth-order relation,

$$R[X_1, \cdots, X_n] \tag{15}$$

The general decomposition procedure can be given in terms of a relative product. A relation R is a relative product of the relations R_1 and R_2 if the following condition is satisfied:

$$(xRy) \leftrightarrow [(xR_1z) \cap (zR_2y)] \tag{16}$$

General decomposition procedure for the systems relation R would consist of finding two new relations R_1 and R_2 for which R is a relative product. The system S is then reticulated into the subsystems

$$\begin{aligned} R_1[X_1, \cdots, X_j, Z] \\ R_2[Z, X_{j+1}, \cdots, X_n] \end{aligned} \tag{17}$$

Consider now the following problem: Given a system with a polyadic nth-order relation (eq. 16) what is the lowest order of the subsystem relations into which this system can be decomposed? The result can be presented in terms of the following theorem:

Theorem

An nth-order system can be:

1. Decomposed into $(n-2)$-triadic relations $\{R_1, \cdots, R_n\}$.
2. Decomposed into dyadic relations if and only if for every triadic relation obtained from (1) the following conditions are satisfied:

(a) $[X_i R_j(X_{i+1}, X_{i+2})] \leftrightarrow \{(X_i R_j^1 Z_j) \cap [Z_j R_j^2 (X_{i+1}, X_{i+2})]\}$ (18)

(b) $Z_j = X_{i+1} \cup X_{i+2}$

Proof: The first part of the theorem can be easily proved by construction. Let us represent the system relation R as a relative product of R_1 and R_2:

$$R = R_1/R_2$$

$$[R_1(Z_1, X_2, X_3)] \cap [R_2(X_1, Z_1, X_4, \cdots, X_n)] \tag{19}$$

Since a new term Z_1 is introduced with the new relations R_1 and R_2, no restrictions are imposed and the decomposition is possible.

Next, R_2 is represented as a new relative product

$$R_2 = R_3/R_4 \tag{20}$$

One then has

$$[R_1(Z_1, X_2, X_3)] \cap [R_3(Z_2, Z_1, X_4)] \cap [R_4(Z_2, X_1, X_5, \cdots, X_n)] \tag{21}$$

Proceeding in the same way, one obtains finally

$$R_{2(k-1)} = R_{2(k-1)+1}/R_{2(k-1)+2}; k = 1 \cdots (n-3)$$

$$[R_1(Z_1, X_2, X_3)] \cap [R_3(Z_2, Z_1, X_4)]$$

$$\cap \cdots \cap [R_{2(n-4)+1}(Z_{n-3}, Z_{n-4}, X_{n-2})]$$

$$\cap [R_{2(n-4)+2}(Z_{n-3}, X_1, X_n)] \tag{22}$$

No restriction is imposed when introducing relative products and, therefore, the decomposition is possible. There are $n-2$ triadic subsystems in the system of eq. 22.

To prove the second part of the theorem, we consider a subsystem from eq. 22; i.e.,

$$R_j(Y_j^1, Y_j^2, Y_j^3) \tag{23}$$

where Y_j^1, Y_j^2, and Y_j^3 are the (respective) terms. We write R_j as a relative product,

$$R_j = R_j^1/R_j^2$$

$$[R_j^1(Z^1, Y_j^3)] \cap [R_j^2(Z^1, Y_j^1, Y_j^2)] \qquad (24)$$

Assume that the condition from eq. 18 is satisfied, so that the medium term is Y_j^2. One then has

$$[R_j^1(Y_j^2 Y_j^3)] \cap [R_j^2(Y_j^2, Y_j^1, Y_j^2)]$$

$$= [R_j^1(Y_j^2, Y_j^3)] \cap [R_j^2(Y_j^1, Y_j^2)] \qquad (25)$$

Subsystem R_j is, therefore, decomposed into binary subsystems. Since this is possible for every j, the system is decomposed into $2(n - 2)$ binary subsystems. This shows sufficiency of the condition from the theorem. To show that this condition is necessary, assume that there exists one triadic subsystem for which the medium term cannot be one of the three terms in the original relation. One would then have

$$R_j(Y_j^1, Y_j^2, Y_j^3)$$

$$R_j = R_j^1/R_j^2 \qquad (26)$$

$$[R_j^1(Y_j^1 Z^1)] \cap [R_j^2(Z^1, Y_j^2, Y_j^3)]$$

Since Z^1 is a new term, the second relation is triadic. By introducing two new relations R_j^1 and R_j^2, the order of relation has not been reduced since R_j^2 is again triadic. This completes the proof.

This theorem shows that, in general, *a higher order system cannot be decomposed into the subsystems with less than triadic relations.*

Perhaps the most important application of this theorem is the introduction of the concept of the state of a system. Consider a system which maps a family of sets X_2 into the set of elements X_1; i.e.,

$$X_1 R X_2(t) \qquad (27)$$

where $X_2(t)$ indicates that the elements of the set are time functions, i.e., the sets in themselves. Assume that the sets $x_2(t) \in X_2(t)$, are finite and have p elements. Equation 27 is of the order $p + 1$ and, according to the theorem, cannot be decomposed into subsystems with order less than triadic. Assume that the elements of $x_2(t)$ are ordered.

$$x_2(t) = [x_2(t_1), x_2(t_2), \cdots, x_2(t_p)] \qquad (28)$$

The system relation (eq. 27) is then

$$x_1 R[x_2(t_1), x_2(t_2), \cdots, x_2(t_p)] \qquad (29)$$

Consider the subset of all the elements of $x_2(t)$ with index higher than j,

$$x_2{}^j(t) = [x_2(t_{j+1}), \cdots, x_2(t_n)] \tag{30}$$

The system relation (eq. 27) is then

$$x_1 R[x_2{}^j(t), x_2{}^{jr}(t)] \tag{31}$$

where $x_2{}^{jr}(t)$ is the remaining subset

$$x_2{}^{jr}(t) = [x_2(t_1), \cdots, x_2(t_j)] \tag{32}$$

We now represent R as a relative product

$$\begin{aligned} X_1 R_1[X_2{}^j(t), Z^j] \\ Z^j R_2 X_2{}^{jr}(t) \end{aligned} \tag{33}$$

The term X_1 now depends upon the medium term Z and does not depend upon the elements of $X_2(t)$ having an index lower than j. Elements of Z represent now the state of the system. The decomposition of eq. 33 can be understood to mean that x_1 depends upon the state of the system at $t = t_j$ and all future elements of x_2, but does not depend upon the prior elements, i.e., those having an index lower than j. In the context of dynamic systems, this is usually expressed by the statement that x_1 does not depend on the values of $x_2(t)$ prior to the time t_j at which the state is known.

This discussion can, of course, be easily extended to the case of infinite sets. For example, if we let the set $x_2(t)$ be of infinite cardinality, we can represent it as the two subsets; e.g.,

$$x_2(t) = \{x_2{}^1(t), x_2{}^2(t)\} \tag{34}$$

with the condition

$$\bigwedge_j \bigwedge_i \{[x_2(t_i) \subset x_2{}^1] \cap [x_2(t_j) \subset x_2{}^2] \leftrightarrow [i < j]\} \tag{35}$$

where $\bigwedge$ is the universal quantifier.

The system relation can then be written as

$$X_1 R[X_2{}^1, X_2{}^2] \tag{36}$$

and, by introducing the relative product, one has

$$\begin{aligned} X_1 R_1[X_2{}^1, Z] \\ Z R(X_2{}^2) \end{aligned} \tag{37}$$

Elements of Z represent the state of the system.

Notice that the concept of the state of a system is introduced as a consequence of the theorem given in this section. Namely, the theorem states that, if one wants to reduce the order of the system relation by eliminating dependence upon all the elements of the subset $X_2{}^2$, the new relation has to be at least triadic, except in the case where the conditions of the theorem are satisfied. The three terms of the triadic relation are, then, input, output, and state.

ATTRIBUTES AND BEHAVIOR OF SYSTEMS

The similarity in the methodology of the sciences and general systems theory, as mentioned in the first section, cannot be overemphasized. The job of a general systems theoretician begins only after a general system is given, e.g., in its explicit form $R[X_1, \cdots, X_n]$. To learn about the system by considering every element in the set of n tuples X_s is clearly impossible. The situation is analogous to the study of a real system without the guidance of an appropriate theory. An infinite number of experiments would then be required. For the understanding of the type of systems under consideration, it is necessary to distinguish the system from some other, possibly similar, systems by means of a relatively small number of statements. These statements should refer to the system in its entirety, as specified by the explicit definition, and not to one particular n tuple.

Consider the cartesian set $X = X_1 * X_2 * \cdots * X_n$ and construct a propositional function $L(x)$ with the individual variable x ranging over the set X. If the proposition $L(x_j)$ is true whenever $x_j \in X_s$, then $L(x)$ is considered to define an attribute of a system.

An attribute of a system is a propositional function defined on X and valid in X_s.

The behavior of a system is defined in the following way:

The behavior of a general system is a set of systems attributes

$$B = \{L_1, \cdots, L_p\} \qquad (38)$$

The important question is how to select a set of attributes $L_1, \cdots, L_k$ which are of importance to a particular system and how to establish their presence or absence. This is, of course, a difficult problem which ultimately has its origin in the domain of a real system, outside the formal studies of general systems. The solution depends on how the real system is to be used. However, a formal study should offer guidance in indicating the kinds of attributes that might be present in a given system. For example, when approaching the study of any system, one would like to know whether the system is open or closed, what its structure is, how the state of the system can be described, etc. There are other properties as, e.g., stability, which might be of special interest in some problems but of minor importance in others.

Whenever one studies or talks about a general system, one uses a language not included in the formal statements which form X_s. Such a statement about the system is called a metastatement and the language used is called a metalanguage. One can, of course, use the same language for the metastatements as for the formal statements of the system, but the two types of statements should be clearly distinguished.

A convenient way to study a general system is to form the metastatements into a new system called a metasystem. A metasystem is selected in such a way that it properly reflects certain attributes of the system but is simpler to study than the original general system.

REPRODUCIBILITY AND CONTROLLABILITY OF SYSTEMS

As examples of attributes of a system which can be studied on the general level, we introduce the concepts of controllability and reproducibility.

First we must introduce the concept of a performance functional. Consider an exemplar of the system behavior. System terms can then be used to determine whether or not the particular behavior of the system is acceptable. Technically, one introduces a mapping from X_s into the set of real numbers Q.

$$\{X \xrightarrow{R} Y\} \xrightarrow{T} Q \tag{39}$$

The problem of controllability refers to the capability of achieving a certain performance by using a given system and a given set of inputs. The definition is the following:

A system is controllable in the set Q_c if and only if for every $q_j \in Q_c$ there exists an $x_j \in X$ such that

$$\{x_j \xrightarrow{R} y_j\} \xrightarrow{T} q_j \tag{40}$$

where x_j is the input of the system and y_j is the output.

In other words, the specified set Q_c is a subset of the set Q_s that can be generated by using all possible systems inputs.

$$Q_c \subseteq Q_s$$

The mapping T usually specifies an optimal point representing the best performance which one could achieve if the system had no constraints. For example, if T is a quadratic functional, the optimal point is the minimum of that functional. We denote the optimal point in q by q_{opt} and introduce the following modified notion of controllability:

The system S is controllable if $Q_c = \{q_{opt}, q_{opt} + \alpha\}$.

The system is not controllable if for all $x \in X; q > (q_{opt} + \alpha)$.

Another concept is related to the capability of the system to reproduce certain outputs. This concept is called reproducibility and is introduced on a local basis by using dense sets. We have the following definition:

Definition

System S is reproducible in the set $Y_r \subset Y_s$ if there exists a subset $Y_{rd} \subset Y_r$ so that:

1. Y_{rd} is dense in Y_r.
2. For every $y_j \in Y_{rd}$ there exists an $x_j \in X$ such that $y_j = T(x_j)$, i.e.,

$$\exists x_j \wedge y_j \{[(x_j \in X_s) \cap (y_j \in Y_{rd})] \leftrightarrow [y_j = T(x_j)]\} \qquad (41)$$

Requirements for the density of the subset in Y in which the reproducibility of the system is evaluated is introduced to avoid the possibility of recognizing a system as reproducible if it can generate only a set of isolated points in the output space Y_s. Namely, for a given multivariable system, one can always find some isolated points in Y_s for which the system relation and inputs will be just right so that the outputs can be reproduced. However, reproducibility has a full meaning only if all the points which are close enough can be reproduced.

A general method for testing reproducibility in this sense is based on the following theorem:

Theorem

System $S = YTX$ is *non*reproducible in the subset Y_{rd} if:

1. There exist two relations R_1 and R_2 whose relative product is the system relation $T = R_1/R_2$, i.e., $[YTZ] \leftrightarrow \{(YR_1Z) \cap (ZR_2X)\}$.

2. The common term Z of the relative product T is a subset of the space Y' that is of lower cardinality than Y, i.e.,

$$Z = Y' = \{\langle y_1, \cdots, y_i \rangle\} \qquad i < n$$
$$Y = \{\langle y_1, \cdots, y_n \rangle\} \qquad\qquad (42)$$

In other words,

$$[YTX] \leftrightarrow \{(YR_1Y') \cap (Y'R_2X)\} \qquad (43)$$

Proof: Condition that an R_1 exists denotes the existence of a mapping of the subset Y' into the set Y,

$$Y' \xrightarrow{R_1} Y$$

Denote the subset of all points in Y which satisfies eq. 43 as $V \subset Y$. Consider a point in V: $\mathbf{y}_v \in V$, i.e., $\mathbf{y}_v$ is a reproducible point. Point $\mathbf{y}_v$ is a vector $\mathbf{y}_v = [y_1(t), y_2(t)_1, \cdots, y_n(t)]$. Let the vector space Y have the metric which relates to the metric in the component spaces in the following way:

$$d[\mathbf{y}_1, \mathbf{y}_{11}] = \sum_{j=1}^{m} d[y_{1j}(t), y_{11j}(t)] \tag{44}$$

To every element $\mathbf{y}'(t) = [y_1(t), \cdots, y_i(t)]$, eq. 43 uniquely defines an element of the remaining set $\mathbf{y}''(t) = [y_{i+1}(t), \cdots, y_n(t)]$: $Y'' = \sim[Y \cap Y']$: $\mathbf{y}''(t) \in Y''$. In other words, to every $\mathbf{y}'(t)$ corresponds a unique element $\mathbf{y}(t)$ or $\mathbf{y}''(t)$.

Consider now the neighborhood of the point $\mathbf{y}_v = [y'(t), y''(t)]$; $K[\mathbf{y}_v, \epsilon]$. For any internal point $\mathbf{y}_s = [\mathbf{y}'_s, \mathbf{y}''_s]$ of the neighborhood K, one has

$$d[\mathbf{y}_v, \mathbf{y}_s] < \epsilon \tag{45}$$

Assume that $\mathbf{y}_s \in V$, i.e., satisfies, i.e., $\mathbf{y}_s$ is a reproducible point. The distance function is now

$$d_s = d[\mathbf{y}_v, \mathbf{y}_s] = \sum_{j=1}^{m} d[y_{vj}(t), y_{sj}(t)]$$

$$= \sum_{j=1}^{i} d[y'_{vj}(t), y'_{sj}(t)] + \sum_{j=i+1}^{m} d[y''_{vj}(t), y''_{sj}(t)] \tag{46}$$

Consider now the point $\mathbf{y}_z$ which has all the elements but one the same as $\mathbf{y}_v$, the remaining element being the same as $\mathbf{y}_s$. Clearly $\mathbf{y}_z$ is not a reproducible point.

$$\mathbf{y}_z = [y'_{v1}(t), \cdots, y''_{vm-1}(t), y''_{sm}(t)] \tag{47}$$

The distance function for $\mathbf{y}_z$ is now

$$d_z = d[\mathbf{y}_v, \mathbf{y}_z] = d[y''_{vm}(t), y''_{sm}(t)] \tag{48}$$

It is apparent that

$$d_z < d_s \tag{49}$$

This means that to every point y_s inside the neighborhood $K(y_v, \epsilon)$ there corresponds a point closer to y_v which does not belong to the set V. In other words, no matter how small in a neighborhood one selects $K(y_v, \epsilon)$,

$\epsilon > 0$, there is always an inside point in K which does not belong to V. Since set V is its own closure $V = \overline{V}$, this means that the set V is nowhere a dense set. This completes the proof.

Importance of the theorem stems from the fact that it offers a general method for establishing non-reproducibility of a system. Since existence of the relation YR_1Y' is sufficient for a system to be non-reproducible in a set Y, it suffices to exhibit the existence of such a relation.

The method for testing reproducibility can be now described in the following way:

To show nonreproducibility of a system, it suffices to derive starting from the system relations a relation among the outputs (or their properties as required by the metric) in which the inputs will not be present.

In its generality, the derived method for testing reproducibility is similar to the methods for testing different attributes of the systems behavior, e.g., Hurwitz criteria or Lyapunov functions, etc. The principal weakness of the method is that it is only existential and does not indicate which technique should be used to construct the constraining relation R_1.

GOAL-SEEKING BEHAVIOR

In the discussions thus far we have always considered a system as a relation among the terms without specifying the meaning which can be attached to these terms with respect to the systems behavior. Yet, as was emphasized in the section entitled "Basic Characteristics of the Theory," it is the meaning given to various terms that distinguishes general systems theory from a mathematical discipline. Every term in a system description has a meaning relevant to the systems behavior which is different from the meaning conventionally assumed in mathematical studies of formal systems.

There are two principal avenues for conducting discourse about systems and, consequently, two contexts in which to give meaning to system terms. These two contexts differ principally in the relation of the observer to the system. In the first approach, one considers the system from the outside and defines its behavior in terms of the mapping of one subset of terms (inputs and states) into another. This way of looking at the system is termed the terminal approach. In the second approach one has knowledge of certain invariable aspects of the system which reflect its goal. Also, one is aware of the activities of the system which are responsible for the goal seeking. This approach is consequently called the goal-seeking approach. The goal-seeking activities are again transformations among some specified system terms, but the system attributes which specify the system's behavior now refer to the particular meaning given to these transformations.

In the discussions in the previous sections, the terminal approach has been used. To develop the goal-seeking approach, the basic concepts of decision-making, control, adaptation, self-organization, etc., must be introduced on a similar, definite basis as were the concepts for the terminal approach. Time and space limitation do not allow us to consider the details of the goal-seeking behavior here. We make only the following general remarks: (1) Every system, at least in principle, can be described either via a terminal approach or a goal-seeking approach. It is the relation of the observer to the system and the knowledge which he possesses about the system that determine the approach to be used. There are, of course, systems (e.g., mechanical systems) where the goals are either unknown or, to our best knowledge, nonexistent. In these cases the introduction of a goal-seeking description is artificial or trivial. We do not feel that one should be too concerned with such special cases, since, for most interesting systems, both approaches have been successfully used. (2) The behavior of goal-seeking systems is much more complex than the behavior of terminal systems. (3) The behavior of goal-seeking systems is much less understood than the behavior of terminal systems.

If a system can be successfully described by either of the approaches, terminal or goal-seeking, and if the former is simpler, then why do we need the latter? The answer, essentially, lies in the possibility for using the system description to predict the system's behavior. That is, if one has the goal-seeking description of a system's behavior, one has far more powerful means of predicting the system behavior under conditions which are different from those existing in the previously conducted experiments.

Let us illustrate this by an example: Consider an animal subjected to a pair of stimuli. The first stimulus, light, is applied a short interval in advance of the second stimulus, electric shock. The animal can escape from the area under electric voltage by crossing a barrier. By repeating the experiments, a learning curve for the animal can be obtained by plotting escape time versus number of experiments. A typical learning curve is given in Fig. 2. Disregarding some transients, the learning curve has a sharp discontinuity. It occurs roughly at the time when the animal discovers the relation between the light and the shock stimuli, and starts running toward the escape barrier immediately after the light appears.

It is apparent that in order to describe the discontinuous learning curve in Fig. 2, one cannot use the same stimuli-response transformation obtained for the same animal under different conditions, e.g., those resulting in a continuous learning curve. Therefore, if one wants to explain the behavior of a learning system under different conditions one has to have better knowledge of the learning process inside the system itself. In such a situation, a model based on the goal-seeking approach is very powerful. For example, if one is able to discover the method used by the system for making the decision to switch from one mode of behavior described by the exponential curve to the other mode described by the horizontal line, one would be in a position to describe the behavior of the system for a variety of conditions without having to conduct specific experiments.

Some basic concepts for the case of simpler goal-seeking systems have already been stated in full generality. However, goal-seeking systems may be very complex and may have a large number of different and conflicting goals as well as a corresponding number of goal-seeking subsystems. Although some progress toward the formalization of the theory for these systems has been made in an initial

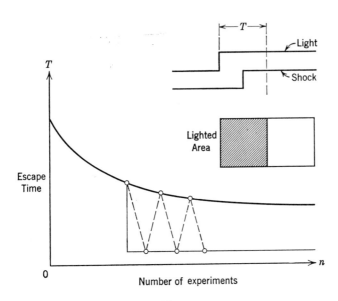

FIG. 2.

study of the so-called multilevel systems, there is still considerable work to be done in this direction. At the same time, this might well be an avenue offering a great return for research effort on general systems theory.

REFERENCES

1. Bertalanfy, L., "An Outline of General Systems Theory," *The British Journal of the Philosophy of Science*, **1**, No. 2 (1950).
2. Curry, H. B., *Outlines of a Formalist Philosophy of Mathematics*, North Holland Co., Amsterdam, 1951.
3. Ashby, W. R., *Introduction to Cybernetics*, John Wiley and Sons, New York, 1955.
4. Boulding, K., "General Systems Theory-Skeleton of Science," *General Systems Yearbook*, **1**, University of Michigan, Ann Arbor (1956).
5. Zadeh, L., "From Circuit Theory to Systems Theory," *Proceedings IRE*, May (1962).
6. Mesarović, M. D., and Eckman, D. P., "On Some Basic Concepts of a General Systems Theory," *Proceedings of the Third International Conference on Cybernetics*, Namur, Belgium (1961).
7. Mesarović, M. D., "Towards the Development of a General Systems Theory," *Neue Technik* (August 1963).
8. Mesarović, M. D., "On Self-Organizational Systems," in *Self-Organizing Systems*, Spartan Press, Washington, D. C., 1962.
9. Mesarović, M. D., "Self-Organizing Control Systems," in *Symposium on Discrete Adaptive Processes, AIEE* (1962).
10. Smullyan, R. M., *Theory of Formal Systems*, Princeton University Press, Princeton, N. J., 1961.
11. Mesarović, M. D., *General Systems Theory*, Notes from the class lectures delivered at Case Institute, 1960.
12. Curry, H. B., *Foundation of Mathematical Logic*, McGraw-Hill Book Co., New York, 1963.
13. Mesarović, M. D., *The Control of Multivariable Systems*, MIT Press and John Wiley and Sons, New York, 1960.

CHAPTER 2

GENERAL SYSTEMS AS A
POINT OF VIEW

KENNETH E. BOULDING

(A Small Cry of Distress, from a Not Very Mathematical Man)
I'm like a rat within a maze,
When faced with sigma's i's and j's,
And problems soon become enigmas
When wrapped in i's and j's and sigma's.

K. B

I teach a course in general systems as part of the Honors Program of the University of Michigan.* I get an excellent cross section of the undergraduate seniors taking the Honors Program in a wide variety of departments. After taking it one year, a student came to me and said, "I haven't learned a thing in this course but I have got a new point of view." I confess I was encouraged by this remark and felt that the course had probably been justified. I hoped, of course, that the student had picked up a certain amount of information at least about some of the more exciting intellectual developments which are going on in our day. I presume he must have learned something or he would not have obtained a new point of view. I must confess, however, that giving a new point of view rather than imparting information as such is one of the main objectives of the course, which is exactly why I have called it "general systems."

I have implied above that general systems is a point of view rather than a body of doctrine. In the future it may develop into a body of doctrine, for it is difficult to find any intellectual movement which does not. Perhaps, indeed, this is inevitable and indeed desirable. One cannot remain forever perched on a point of view, however pleasing the prospect, and one must go down and occupy the land. At the moment it would be presumptuous to claim that there is any clearly defined body of theory which could be identified with the name "general

* It is listed in the University of Michigan catalog (1962/63) as College Honors 498.

systems." Nevertheless there is a general systems point of view and there is what DeSolla Price has called "an invisible college," of people who recognize each other as possessing this point of view. What I wish to do, therefore, is to try to identify some of the main elements of the point of view even though this may represent the first slippery step toward a body of doctrine and may, indeed, reveal the distressing fact that there is not one point of view in general systems but a large number.

Any point of view depends on certain value presuppositions and positions of the viewer, for we all view the world from some high-valued peak within our own welfare function. Things which we value more highly loom more closely in our mental landscape. This I call the iron law of perspective. I know of no real escape from this iron law. Even the attempt in the world of art to look at things from all sides, as the cubist does, sometimes ends up by looking at them from no side at all, and results in breaking up order into something peril-ously akin to chaos. Even if our welfare function sets a high value on the virtues of objectivity and a Cartesian clarity, we still view the world from a perspective, for those things which are clearly quantifiable and orderly will occupy the foreground, and we will relegate Celtic twilights, mystical experience, and all things of clouded and brooding significance to the jungle edges of our tight little intellectual clearing. The only way to bend the iron law of perspective is to know as well as we can the point from which we view. Then we can at least know intellectually, even if not perhaps viscerally, that the looming fore-ground is not as large nor the shadowy background as small as it seems to us. Not even general systems, broad as its landscape claims to be, can escape this iron law, and we must therefore look frankly at the value presuppositions which are likely to lead to a general systems point of view.

The first of these presuppositions is a prejudice in favor of system, order, regularity, and nonrandomness (all these words being roughly synonymous), and a prejudice against chaos and randomness. Along with the poets, the general systems type of person has "rage for order," as Austin Warren has called it. He will certainly be fond of mathe-matics, almost certainly fond of music, and he may have a half-ashamed passion for the eighteenth century.

The next prejudice is a simple corollary from the first, that is, the whole empirical world is more interesting ("good") when it is orderly. It is to the orderly segments of the world, therefore, that the general systems man is attracted. He loves regularity, his delight is in the law, and a law to him is a path through the jungle.

Now comes the main article of the general systems faith, for the first two, after all, he shares with many scientific specialists; that is, the order of the empirical world itself has order which might be called order of the second degree. If he delights to find a law, he is ecstatic when he finds a law about laws. If laws in his eyes are good, laws about laws are simply delicious and are most praiseworthy objects of search. The critic may perhaps argue that the hunger and thirst after this order of the second degree is merely a passion for the familiar. The general systems man, he will say, is the sort who would be reminded of Pittsburgh even in the middle of Bangkok, simply because both are cities and have streets with people in them. The critic (I somehow visualize him as a historian in a high collar) has a passion not so much for order and familiarity as for things that are peculiar, unique, strange, and disjoint. As a general systems man, I will visit him in his lonely eyrie, but even there I will probably be reminded of something—much to his annoyance. To avoid circumlocutions, let me call my general systems man a generalist and my high-collared historian a particularist. The generalist rejoices when he sees, for instance, that in all growth patterns there are significant common elements, such as nucleation, structural adjustment in the parts of the system, diminishing returns to scale, and ogive curves. A particularist brushes this aside and rejoices in the fact that the growth of the flower is so different from the growth of a crystal, or the growth of Rome so different from the growth of Athens.

Because of his rage for order, our generalist is likely to set a high value on quantification and mathematization, for these are great helps in establishing order. There is, therefore, a prejudice in their favor and a desire to use them as far as (or even farther than) they can usefully go. Even the most passionate generalist, however, is likely to admit that there are elements of the empirical world, such as aesthetics, love, literature, poetry, human relations, religion, etc., which resist quantification and yet are orderly in their own bizarre fashion. The generalist, however, has a strong desire to discover a continuum, which he enjoys perceiving, between quantifiable and nonquantifiable order. He sees poetry as a nonrandom sequence of words, music as a nonrandom sequence of notes, different in kind but not in form from any nonrandom sequence of numbers.

Order is always perceived as an abstraction from the complex flux of reality. It is indeed usually seen as a relation among abstractions themselves, such as numbers, lines, or spaces. The difference, perhaps, between the general systems man and the pure mathematician is that, whereas the mathematician is content with the mere perception and demonstration of abstract order, the general systems man is interested in looking for empirical referents of these systems and laws of abstract order, for it is this ability to perceive the infinite particularity of the empirical world as examples of an abstract order which gives that world its unity and, indeed, makes it in some sense "good." To justify the ways of God to man is an important task, even for atheists, and it is done by tracing the golden threads of abstract order through the infinitely fragmented dark and light mosaic of the world of experience.

Thus the mathematician is content with having discovered the exquisite abstract order implied in the exponential function and the elegant properties of the strange number e (2.718). The general systems man seizes upon this as the expression of a general law of growth at a constant rate, of which over short periods there are innumerable examples in the empirical world, whether this be the growth of a crystal, of a living body, of an organization, of a whole economy, or perhaps of the universe itself. The mathematician devises an equation which describes a familiar ogive curve; the general systems man regards this as a pattern which is repeated over and over again in the empirical world, as we move from one equilibrium system to another at a different level. The mathematician sees the solution of simultaneous equations as a problem in abstract order; the general systems man perceives this as descriptive of the equilibrium of an ecosystem or of a price system. The mathematician develops difference equations or differential equations as expressions of a relationship among purely abstract concepts; the general systems man considers them descriptive of a large class of dynamic processes, whether one which keeps the planets in their courses, one which determines the movement of a falling body, or one which describes the movement of an economic system through time. Not all mathematical equations or relationships have empirical referents. I find it hard to conceive, for instance, any real empirical referent to the series of prime numbers, although I have one student who is working on this problem. When an empirical referent can be found, however, there is great rejoicing in the general systems heaven.

The process of finding empirical referents to formal laws can easily take either one of two possible directions. We may find some elegant relationship in the world of abstract mathematics and then look around the world of experience to see if we can find anything like it, or we may patiently piece out a rough empirical order in the world of experience and then look to the abstract world of mathematics to codify, simplify it, and relate it to other laws. A good example of this phenomenon is "Zipf's law." Zipf was a Professor of German at Harvard who conceived a passion for counting things and for plotting the frequencies of organized distributions on double logarithmic paper. A purely empirical law seemed to emerge which showed that almost all organized distributions—e.g., the size of cities, the frequencies of words, the intervals between notes in music, or the distribution of income—when plotted on double logarithmic paper turned out to be a straight line. Following this purely empirical observation, which itself may be open to some questioning, several attempts have been made, the most successful perhaps by Herbert Simon, to develop mathematical models which will produce organized distributions having this property. Going to the other extreme, we find whole branches of mathematics which have been developed by pure mathematicians without even a thought of empirical referents which have later turned out to be of enormous significance in exploring the more refined aspects of the empirical world, especially in physics. Even in the social sciences, the mathematical theory of convex sets was developed long before it turned out to have an important empirical referent in linear programming. The value system of the general systems man is, therefore, different from that of the pure mathematician. The famous Cambridge toast, "Here is to pure mathematics, and may it never be any damned good to anybody," has been reworded by him to "Here's to pure mathematics, and may it soon be good for something" or "Here's to empirical regularity, may we soon find a mathematical excuse for it." Whatever his other virtues, the general systems man is irretrievably impure in his tastes and his fundamental value system.

Simply because any point of view implies perspective as we have seen, and perspective is illusion interpreted to mean reality, the interpretation may break down. The near things may be perceived as large, and the far things as small *in fact*. A point of view, therefore, implies certain dangers of misperception, and the general systems point of view is no exception to this rule. The general systems man, if he is honest, must admit these dangers and be prepared to face them. Some of the dangers are obvious and are avoided fairly easily; others are more subtle and require a highly sensitized perception.

An obvious danger frequently pointed out is that an interest in the whole empirical world and the attempt to view this world as a whole lead to superficiality and dilettantism. The whole empirical world in our days, at least, is far beyond the capacity of any one mind to know. My wife has a standard formula, for which I endeavor to be grateful, for deflating me whenever my general systems visions soar too high. She says simply, "If you are going to be the great integrator you ought to know something." Even the most renaissance of renaissance men in our days cannot hope to know more than a very small fraction of what is known by somebody. The general systems man, therefore, is constantly taking leaps in the dark, constantly jumping to conclusions on insufficient evidence, constantly, in fact, making a fool of himself. Indeed, the willingness to make a fool of oneself should be a requirement for admission to the Society of General Systems Research, for this willingness is almost a prerequisite to rapid learning.

One obvious safeguard against the worst forms of superficiality is a firm foundation of knowledge in at least one empirical discipline. Before the general systems man takes off into the outer space of his ignorance, he ought at least to have a launching pad in some discipline where he can reasonably claim to be an expert. He must have the courage not merely to take refuge in a well-tended little plot of specialized knowledge but he should also feel that his most important and most secure contributions comes when he brings back and applies to his own specialized fields the insights which have come to him during his aerial surveys of the whole empirical universe. The ideal general systems man must be willing to talk nonsense outside his own field but must be equally unwilling to talk nonsense inside it.

A danger less readily perceived, but perhaps characteristic of the whole scientific enterprise, arises because the "rage for order" leads to the perception of order where, in fact, no order exists. Alex Bavelas has reported (orally) some experiments in which he has given his subjects random sequences or patterns, for instance, sequences drawn from a table of random numbers, and asked them to deduce any law or principle which governs the sequence. His subjects almost invariably not only see order in these random sequences but also vigorously defend the order which they have perceived when he challenges it, and they become angry with him when he suggests that sequences are, in fact, random. I once had a sad experience in teaching business cycles when I began by asking the class to plot random sequences on a graph, the sequences being derived, for instance, by throwing dice or by pulling numbers out of a hat. Such sequences, when plotted, have all the appearance of time series of most economic variables, and I confess my objective was to shatter the naive faith that the student might have in the strictly nonrandom character of economic fluctuations. Unfortunately, my experiments backfired. One student, who was something of a gambler, thought that he did, in fact, perceive a law in the sequence of throws of dice and spent most of the semester trying to find what it was. He did not, as far as I recall, get a very high grade in the course, and I never did find out whether his researches paid off financially.

It may be, therefore, that the same rage for order which produces a sonnet produces, in its pathological form, the rigid and compulsive gambler at the slot machine. In its pathological forms, too, the rage for order creates race prejudice, stereotyping, international conflict, MacCarthyism, and so on. Unfortunately, I know of no very good remedy for this except a constant watchfulness. As far as I know, there is no absolutely secure way of testing the randomness of any finite sequence. All empirically perceived regularities, therefore, have a degree of ambiguity in them, and in some cases, especially in social systems, the ambiguities are so severe that the problem of accurate social perception seems almost impossible. William Gamson, for instance, of the University of Michigan, has reported (orally) that the Cuban crisis of October 1962 reinforced almost in everybody his image of the international system which he had previously held, no matter how inconsistent these images might be. In the extreme case of the schizophrenic, *all* the messages which he receives reinforce the unreal image of the world which he possesses, and even much that passes for normal behavior is perilously close to this pattern.

Our particularist critic now seems to have turned from a high-collared historian into a soft-shirted semanticist. There is a certain intellectual syndrome that includes both general systems and general semantics, improbable as this may seem. Actually, this may turn out to be a very useful combination. The insistence of general semantics on the particular, even to the extent, perhaps, of extending the semantic incantation to "this general system is not that general system," is nevertheless a useful corrective to the more pathological expressions of the rage for order. To talk about truth at all, and to hold conversations about it, we must look for general systems. Nevertheless, it is useful to heed William Blake who said that truth always lies in minute particulars. Too much obsession with the particular, however, and too much semantic nervousness may prohibit conversation altogether, and might even make pictures disintegrate into pointilliste patterns. As Alice in Wonderland so sagely remarked, "What is the use of a book [or for that matter a world] without conversations and pictures?"

If the rage for order has its dangers, a passion for order of the second degree and for the laws of laws, no doubt, exposes us to double jeopardy. A grave danger here is that of drawing false analogies. Analogy seems to have a bad name among philosophers, and though I know of no good study of what makes an analogy false, I am aware that this may simply indicate my ignorance of current philosophical literature. Even the analog computer in these days seems to have been fighting a losing battle with its digital brother, although there are some signs that its greatest usefulness may still lie in the future. Among general systems men the words "homology" and "homomorphism" are "good words," which seem to avoid the unfortunate histories associated with the word "analogy." I must confess that I am not quite sure of the exact difference between analogy and a homology, except that analogy is a bad homology and homology is a good analogy.

The confusion of thought here arises, I suspect, because it is not so much the analogy that is bad as the system which is derived from it. Wherever man is faced with an empirical system of some kind, he has an uncontrollable urge to produce a mental system or an image in his mind which is a model or an explanation of the empirical system he encounters. Empirical systems in the outside world are very complex and, as we all know, it is extremely hard to find out what is their true systematic nature. It is not surprising, therefore, that we argue by analogy from systems we know, or think we know, to systems we think we do not know. Thus, primitive man encounters a strange world of trees, animals, and objects of all kinds which clearly have some systematic properties but whose mysteries he cannot fathom. He is conscious also of himself as a complex system which is guided, however, by the mysterious unity of the "me." It is not surprising, then, that he argues by analogy from himself to the inanimate world, and populates this world with spirits. As he learns that he can placate and move other men by suitable language, it seems reasonable to him that he can also placate the spirits of trees, rocks, and animals by suitable language. Because of the ambiguity of all systems, it takes him a long time to learn that this method is ultimately disappointing. Nevertheless, animism may justly be regarded as the first general system, and the fact that we now regard it as false does not negate the fact that it was a remarkable achievement of the human mind at an early stage.

In the physical sciences, the method of analogy ("What would I feel like if I were a flying stone") has largely been superseded by the development of theoretical systems which are very closely tied to their own particular referents. The internal logic of the theoretical system is tested by reference to the formal principles of mathematics to be sure that the logic comes from its own internal structure and is not borrowed from some system outside. Logic alone, however, will not guarantee that a theoretical system has the right relationship to its empirical referent. To insure such correspondence, the system or the theory must be *tested* against its supposed empirical referent. The fundamental principle of all such testing is to create expectations of the future by means of careful inference from the supposed system and then simply to observe whether this expectation is disappointed or fulfilled. In the experimental method, the expectation is created by acts on the part of the investigator; in the observational method, the expectation is created by projections of past history of the dynamic system. All of this is familiar in the philosophy of science. It is not surprising under these circumstances that physical scientists especially are suspicious of general systems, simply because their own success has been the result of their breaking away from false methods of analogy. The biological sciences, likewise, seemed to have achieved their greatest successes by developing highly special systems with narrow empirical referents, and here again suspicion of general systems as the bearer of false analogies is understandable.

It is in the social sciences, perhaps, that we are most plagued with false analogies and yet have the greatest hope from true ones. The damage done by false analogies has been enormous. In political science, for instance, a great deal of thinking has not risen much above propositions of the type, "The body has a head, therefore, the state must have a king." Social Darwinism is a case of application of a false analogy from the biological sciences to systems which are much more complex. It is an example, indeed, of how dangerous can be the application of an empty theory from one discipline into another discipline. What might be called vulgar evolutionary theory, as summed by the slogan "the survival of the fittest," is an almost completely empty theory, for, if we ask what the fit are fit for, the answer, of course, is to survive; so the theory is a theory of the survival of the surviving, which does not tell us very much. The application of theory of this kind to the social sciences is so misleading as to be positively disastrous.

The dangers of analogies are, of course, not confined to those analogies that cross the disciplines, for even within a single discipline, we still find ourselves in grave errors as a result of what might be called animistic analogy. A good example of this is to be found in economics. One of the major problems of our day is the tremendous gap that exists between systematic economics, or the image of the economy in the minds of the professional economists, and "folk economics," which is the image of the economy in the minds of practically everybody else. Folk economics argues largely by analogy from individual experience to the economic system as a whole, and these analogies are nearly always false and almost invariably result in fallacies of composition. In systematic economics, for instance, expenditure and receipts are exactly the same thing, as one person's expenditure is always somebody else's receipts. In folk economics, which argues by analogy by the individual to the total system, expenditure can be different from receipts. In systematic economics, the national debt is seen clearly as equivalent to the government securities held by the public and, hence, an important constituent of the financial system capable of being used as an instrument of cybernetic control. In folk economics, the national debt is seen simply as a burden and a moral evil to be gotten rid of as soon as possible. It is hardly an exaggeration to say that the attitudes engendered by folk economics are enormously costly in that they prevent the proper operation of our economic system, and it is quite conceivable that they might even be disastrous. Even the social scientists, therefore, do not have to be persuaded that analogy is dangerous.

I seem to have made general systems sound so dangerous that I almost appear to be putting forward a motion for the dissolution of the Society for General Systems Research. I must confess, however, that this is something of a rhetorical trick. It is now Act V, and I must rescue my heroine from villains who have threatened her. The crucial question is, "At what point does the method of special theoretical systems and empirical testing break down?" I argue that it breaks down at two points. One is at the point of the Heisenberg principle of indeterminacy where the information that the investigator is endeavoring to extract from the system has the same order of magnitude of the system itself, so that information cannot be applied to or withdrawn from the system without changing it. This principle was first noticed in physics, but it is of increasing importance as we move up through the biological to the social sciences. We frequently cannot investigate the living organism without killing it, we cannot make a statement about the economic system without changing it, we cannot ask a man a question without changing his opinion, and we cannot put an anthropologist into a tribe without changing its culture. In other words, we have to recognize the fact that we do not have an outside observer, but that the investigator is always an intimate part of the system and cannot make his own observations or develop and propound new knowledge without changing the system that he is investigating.

The second point of breakdown in the classical scientific method of special systems and empirical testing occurs in the study of systems that are in themselves probabilistic or stochastic, and in which the nature of the order itself is not deterministic (i.e., events occur with the probability of one), but in which (in the essential nature of the system itself) events occur with the probability of less than one. In such a system, a single observation tells us nothing about the probability of the occurrence of the event observed. The method of the testing of expectations, therefore, breaks down simply because the expectation is that of a probability of an event, not of its certainty. In October 1962, for instance, we managed to avoid a nuclear war, but this fact in itself tells us nothing about whether the probability of nuclear war at that time was 5% or 95%. Even if the probability had been 95%, we might still have picked the one white ball out of the bag with 19 black balls in it, and the mere fact that we picked a white ball out the bag tells us nothing about how many black balls there were. Physical systems in the small range, biological systems in the middle range, and social systems throughout their whole range are of this probabilistic nature, and also have Heisenberg principles built right into them. The two properties, indeed, seem to go along together.

We now see the success of the method of special systems and empirical testing in physics as a fortunate accident, and, as a result, the fact that the systems investigated were gross in nature and with a very small probabilistic element. For Heisenberg systems where information and the observer are of the same order of the magnitude of the system, and for the closely related probabilistic systems, the method of general systems is a necessity. Weak and dangerous as it may be, it is the only avenue open to us towards greater knowledge. This explains, I think, the increasing interest in simulation in both social and biological sciences. Where systems cannot be investigated without changing them profoundly, and where they cannot be tested because of the probabilistic elements involved, the only road to knowledge left is that of simulation, that is, the construction of grosser systems which have some kind of one-to-one relationship with the systems we really want to investigate, and which are so gross that they can, in fact, be investigated. It is perhaps too much to claim that the method of simulation is a child of general systems, but it is certainly highly consistent with the general systems point of view.

The great problem here is how to defend ourselves in the case of ambiguous systems and ambiguous perceptions from the danger of allowing value presuppositions to govern our perception of the system. The great psychological problem is the rigidity of the image, and it is associated with values which seem to be involved with the identity of the person. People often construct their own personal identity around some ideology to which they give assent. When a man says *I am* a

Baptist, or a Republican, or a Communist, he is, in effect, identifying his person with the ideology which he holds. A threat to the ideology, therefore, is seen as a threat to the person, and it is not surprising that it is strongly resisted. Under these circumstances, we become immune and deaf to any messages which seem to contradict the ideology. Either we reject the inferences which gave rise to the disappointed expectations or we deny that expectations have, in fact, been disappointed, because of the ever-present ambiguity in the interpretations of the message inputs.

I argue that there are two closely related remedies for this disease. One is the lessening of the ambiguities in perception itself largely through the quantification, indexing, and systematic processing of large quantities of information. A good example of this process is the impact of the development of national income statistics which were pioneered in the National Bureau of Economic Research in the 1920's, taken over by the Department of Commerce in the 1930's, and became, as it were, public property and a familiar element in political discourse in the 1940's. This has made our perception of economic fluctuations much less ambiguous. In 1931 it was still possible for quite intelligent people to argue about whether or not there was a depression. Herbert Hoover, indeed, in his memoirs says that apple selling became very profitable at this time, and a lot of people went into it. In the 1960's no such argument is possible. There are, of course, very real problems of interpretation and measurement, some of which are indeed inherently insoluble. Nevertheless, we now cannot have a downturn in the economy for even two or three months without most people in decision-making positions being aware of it, and this awareness in itself creates a strong desire to do something about it. One of the great needs of the present is a similar information processing system in international systems. At the moment we rely on a hopelessly obsolete way of information collecting and processing, involving diplomats, the CIA, and a State Department almost entirely innocent of social science, all of which contribute to a magnificent system for the corruption of information. It is not surprising that the international system works so badly and is so fantastically dangerous.

The second line of defense against the misperception of ambiguous systems is the general systems point of view itself. If analogy is dangerous and leads to the development of untrue systems, the remedy is not to throw it overboard altogether, for there are situations in which no other method of systems development is open to us. The remedy for false analogy is not *no* analogy but *true* analogy. This involves the development of a critique of analogy and a theory of simulation.

Although we are still unfortunately a long way from this goal, it is, nevertheless, one of the principal concerns of the general systems enterprise. It has been said before that the business of science is to detect similarities amid apparent differences, and differences amid apparent similarities. If the first is a peculiar task of the generalist and the second the particularist, this merely points out the fact that these two views are complementary rather than competitive.

Let me now return to the question which was implicit in my opening statement, as to whether general systems should, in fact, be taught especially to undergraduates or even graduate students. Some may argue that general systems is a heady brew likely to distract students from the main business of acquiring competence in their own particular field, and that, even if it is justified at all, nobody without at least two Ph.D.'s should be allowed to touch it. I confess that I have had one or two experiences with students which indicate that the danger is not wholly unreal. It is possible for students of a certain type to get so caught up with the excitement of the general systems point of view that they try to introduce it prematurely and inappropriately even into a Ph.D. dissertation. The acquisition of a specialized discipline always involves a certain amount of heavy, dull work, and it is to be expected that occasionally a brilliant but not too solid student will kick over the traces and try to take the short-cuts to knowledge which the general systems approach may seem to offer. Even good advice and firm handling may not wholly eliminate this risk. Nevertheless, I believe that this is a risk worth taking. Dullness and a lack of a sense of significance are the greatest enemies facing the intellectual life. It is a terrible commentary on our whole educational system that we still take the eager young minds which come out of high school and knock all the eagerness and enthusiasm out of them by the long grind that leads to a Ph.D. Creativity in the sciences as well as in the arts comes from a combination of excitement, hard work, and discipline. In our educational system it is easier to teach discipline than excitement, and the discipline often destroys the excitement. If a general systems point of view can be developed alongside the acquisition of a specialized discipline, it will enrich the work in the discipline itself, simply because of the intellectual excitement that the general systems pont of view can engender. What we are in danger of losing in our universities is a feeling that a great intellectual task is still to be accomplished. Intellectual excitement is generated at the point where the individual feels that what he is doing is advancing, in however small a degree, some intellectual task. Excitement, of course, is not a substitute for solid achievement, but it is a very good complement, and it seems to me we are in much more danger from dullness than from overstimulation. I am not suggesting, of course, that only the general systems point of view creates intellectual excitement. A student can get a great sense of excitement from being on the frontier of a particular discipline. A general systems point of view is, however, important in creating a feeling of intellectual community and of a common task, and in this sense the excitement that it generates may be peculiarly beneficial.

CHAPTER 3

THE CONCEPT OF STATE IN SYSTEM THEORY

L. A. ZADEH *

A system is a big black box
Of which we can't unlock the locks,
And all we can find out about
Is what goes in and what comes out.

Perceiving input-output pairs,
Related by parameters,
Permits us, sometimes, to relate
An input, output, and a state.
If this relation's good and stable
Then to predict we may be able,
But if this fails us—heaven forbid!
We'll be compelled to force the lid!

K. B.

INTRODUCTION

The concept of state has long played an important role in the physical sciences, particularly in the fields of thermodynamics, mechanics, and physics. It was, and still is, usual in these fields to define the state of a system in a heuristic manner as a number or a set of numbers, which collectively contains all the information about the past of the system that is relevant to the determination of its future behavior.

It was toward the turn of this century that the concept of state was given a more precise formulation by H. Poincare [1] in the context of his theory of dynamical systems—a theory which was subsequently more fully developed by G. Birkhoff,[2] A. A. Markov,[3] V. V. Nemytskii,[4] and L. S. Pontryagin.[5]

In recent years, the concept of state has come to play also an important role in such new fields as information theory, decision theory,

* This work was supported in part by a grant from the National Aeronautics and Space Administration.

and optimal control. Essentially, in these as well as other fields, the notion of state enters primarily in connection with the mathematical characterization of the systems which are the object of study. The growing complexity and the wide diversity of such systems have produced a need for a more general formulation of the notion of state, a formulation which is not limited in its applicability to systems of a particular physical or mathematical form, e.g., thermodynamical systems, dynamical systems in the sense of Birkhoff, systems having a finite number of states, systems whose behavior is governed by differential equations, etc.

To define the notion of state in a way which would make it applicable to all systems is a difficult, perhaps impossible, task. In this chapter, our more modest objective is to sketch an approach that seems to be more natural as well as more general than those employed heretofore, but still falls short of complete generality. Specifically, we shall make the restrictive assumption that the systems under consideration are (a) deterministic, i.e., do not contain sources of noise or probabilistic (random) components, and (b) nonanticipative, i.e., operate only on the present and past (and not on the future) values of the inputs to which they are subjected.

To place the more general notion of state in a clearer perspective, it will be helpful to review briefly the ways in which the concept of state is introduced (a) in the theory of dynamical systems, and (b) in the theory of automata. This we do in the following section.

THE NOTION OF STATE IN DYNAMICAL SYSTEMS AND AUTOMATA

Definition 1

Following Nemytskii, a *dynamical system* is defined as a group of transformations $\{R_t\}$ on a separable metric space R, with $\{R_t\}$ having the following properties:

1. R_t is defined for all t in the interval $-\infty < t < \infty$.

2. Let $q = f(p, t)$ denote the image of a point p in R under R_t. Then f has the group property:

$$f(p, t_0 + t) = f(f(p, t_0), t) \tag{1}$$

3. The group R_t is continuous in the sense that, for all t_0 and P_0 and all sequences $\{t_n\}$ and $\{p_n\}$ which converge respectively to t_0 and p_0, we have

$$\lim_{n \to \infty} f(p_n, t_n) = f(p_0, t_0)$$

A point p of R constitutes a *state* of the dynamical system in question. Thus, $q = f(p, t)$ represents the state of the system at time t given that the system was in state p at time $t = 0$.

The above definition of a dynamical system was motivated primarily by problems arising in celestial mechanics and, more generally, in the dynamics of rigid bodies. For this reason, it makes no explicit provision for input and output. However, all that is necessary to introduce the input and output is a slight modification in the definition in question. One such modified definition was given in a recent paper by Kalman.[6] The latter definition is reproduced in the following.

Definition 2

A dynamical system is a mathematical structure defined by the following axioms:

1. There is given a *state space* Σ and a set of values of *time* Θ at which the behavior of the system is defined; Σ is a topological space and Θ is an ordered topological space which is a subset of the real numbers.

2. There is given a topological space Ω of functions of time, defined on Θ, which are the admissible *inputs* to the system. Ω is a topological space.

3. For any initial time t_0 in Θ, any initial state x_0 in Σ, and any input u in Ω defined for $t \geqq t_0$, the future states of the system are determined by the transition function $\phi : \Omega \times \Theta \times \Theta \times \Sigma \to \Sigma$, which is written as $\phi_u(t; t_0, x_0) = x_t$. This function is defined only for $t \geq t_0$. Moreover, for any $t_0 \leq t_1 \leq t_2$ in Θ, any x_0 in Σ, and any fixed u in Ω defined over $[t_0, t_1] \cap \Theta$, the following relations hold:

$$\phi_u(t_0; t_0, x_0) = x_0 \tag{2}$$

$$\phi_u(t_2; t_0, x_0) = \phi_u(t_2; t_1, \phi_u(t_1; t_0, x_0)) \tag{3}$$

In addition, the system must be *nonanticipatory*, i.e., if $u, v \in \Omega$ and $u \equiv v$ on $[t_0, t] \cap \Theta$, we have

$$\phi_u(t; t_0, x_0) \equiv \phi_v(t; t_0, x_0) \tag{4}$$

4. Every *output* of the system is a function $\psi : \Theta \times \Sigma \to$ reals.

5. The functions ϕ and ψ are continuous with respect to the topologies defined for Σ, Θ, and Ω.

As we shall see later, a serious shortcoming of this definition is that it does not cover those systems whose output is not expressible as a function of the state and time. A simple example of such a system is a differentiator, i.e., a system characterized by the input-output relation $y = du/dt$, where $u(t)$ and $y(t)$ denote respectively the input and output at time t.

The significance of the group property of eqs. 1 and 3 will become clearer in the light of the more general definitions which will be given in the section entitled "The Notion of State." For the present, we turn our attention briefly to the way in which the notion of state is introduced in the theory of automata.[7,8]

Definition 3

A *finite state system* or an *automaton* A is a triple of finite sets Σ, U, and Y, and a pair of mappings

$$f: \Sigma \times U \times T \to \Sigma$$

and

$$g: \Sigma \times U \times T \to Y$$

where T is the set of integers, $T = \{ \cdots, -1, 0, 1, \cdots \}$. The elements of Σ are the *states* of A; the elements of U are the *inputs* to A; and the elements of Y are the *outputs* of A. The time t is assumed to range over T, with the state, input, and output of A at time t denoted by s_t, u_t and y_t respectively. The mappings f and g relate the state at time $t + 1$ and the output at time t to the state and the input at time t. In symbols,

$$s_t = f(s_t, u_t, t) \tag{5}$$

$$y_t = g(s_t, u_t, t) \tag{6}$$

It is of interest to compare this definition with definition 2. In the first place, the analog of the function $\phi_u(t; t_0, x_0)$ which expresses the state of A at time $t \geq t_0$ as a function of the state of A at time t_0 (that is, x_0) and the values of the input u between t and t_0 is the iterated function

$$f(\cdots f(f(s_{t_0}, u_{t_0}, t_0), u_{t_0+1}, t_0 + 1) \cdots, u_t, t) \tag{7}$$

which expresses s_{t+1} as a function of s_{t_0}, t_0, t, and $u_{t_0}, \cdots, u_t$. It is easy to verify that this iterated function has the group property of eq. 3.

In the second place, the expression for the output in the case of a finite-state system is slightly more general than that given by axiom 4, because it allows the output to depend not only on the state and time but also on the input. Thus, to make the class of finite-state systems a subclass of the class of dynamical systems, it is necessary to define ψ as a function from $\Theta \times \Sigma \times \Omega$ into the reals rather than, as in definition 2, from $\Theta \times \Sigma$ into the reals.

There are two points on which the definitions given above are subject to criticism. First, definition 2 is not sufficiently general, even with the modification in the definition of ψ mentioned in the preceding paragraph. Second, and more important, it would be desirable to define a dynamical system as a geometrical object independent of the way in which a state is associated with it. Clearly, neither definition 2 nor definition 3 provide such an intrinsic mode of characterization of a dynamical system.

In the following section, we shall give a simple and natural definition which does not have this shortcoming. After that, we shall introduce the notion of state and deduce some of its basic properties.*

THE NOTION OF AN ORIENTED ABSTRACT OBJECT

Roughly speaking, by an oriented abstract object we mean an abstractly defined system associated with an input (cause) u and an output (effect) y. [Here and in the sequel a symbol such as u will denote a vector-valued time function, with the value of u at time t written as $u(t)$. Thus, unless otherwise specified, it will be understood that u is the set of pairs $\{ (t, u(t)) \mid -\infty < t < \infty \}$. For simplicity, we assume that t ranges over the real line.] Generally, the relation that the system induces between u and y is not one-one. Thus, to a particular input time function u may correspond more than one output time function, and, conversely, to a particular output time function y may correspond more than one input time function.

Before attempting to cast the notion of an oriented abstract object into a more precise form, it will be helpful to introduce the following notation: The symbol $u_{[t_0, \, t_1]}$ represents a *segment* of u over an observation interval $[t_0, t_1]$. More specifically, $u_{[t_0, \, t_1]}$ is the set of pairs $\{ (t, u(t)) \mid t_0 \leq t \leq t_1 \}$. Similarly, for semiclosed observation intervals, we write

$$u_{(t_0, \, t_1]} \overset{\Delta}{=} \{ (t, u(t)) \mid t_0 < t \leq t_1 \} \tag{8}$$

where the symbol $\overset{\Delta}{=}$ stands for "is defined to be."

For simplicity, the symbols $u_{[t_0, \, t_1]}$ and $u_{(t_0, t_1]}$ will frequently be abbreviated to u, which is also the symbol used to denote the time function $u \overset{\Delta}{=} \{ (t, u(t)) \mid -\infty < t < \infty \}$. Generally, the sense in which u must be interpreted will be clear from the context.

Returning to our preliminary discussion of the notion of an oriented abstract object, we note that, when one experiments with a physical device, one usually applies an input time function over an observation interval $[t_0, t_1]$ and measures the corresponding output time function over the same interval. Thus, the result of such an experiment is what might be called an *input-output pair* $(u_{[t_0, t_1]}, y_{[t_0, t_1]})$.

* The approach described in the next two sections is a modified version of that developed in the book by C. A. Desoer and the writer.[9]

If the same input time function is applied to another copy of the device under test, the resulting output may not be the same because the initial excitation of the second copy may be different from that of the first copy. Thus, our definition must reflect the fact that to a given $u_{[t_0, t_1]}$ may correspond more than one $y_{[t_0, t_1]}$.

Let $R_{[t_0, t_1]}$ denote a set of ordered pairs of time functions defined on the observation interval $[t_0, t_1]$; that is,

$$R_{[t_0, t_1]} \overset{\Delta}{=} \{(u_{[t_0, t_1]}, y_{[t_0, t_1]})\} \tag{9}$$

In terms of such sets, an oriented abstract object may be defined as follows.

Definition 4

An *oriented abstract object* A is a family $\{R_{[t_0, t_1]}\}$, $t_0, t_1 \in (-\infty, \infty)$, of sets of ordered pairs of time functions, with a generic pair denoted by (u, y), in which the first component, $u \overset{\Delta}{=} u_{[t_0, t_1]}$, is called an *input segment* or, simply, an *input*, and the second component, $y \overset{\Delta}{=} y_{[t_0, t_1]}$, is called an *output segment* or, simply, an *output*. A pair of time functions (u, y), $u \overset{\Delta}{=} u_{[t_0, t_1]}$, $y \overset{\Delta}{=} y_{[t_0, t_1]}$, is an *input-output pair belonging to* A, written as $(u, y) \in A$, if $(u, y) \in R_{[t_0, t_1]}$ for some t_0, t_1 in $(-\infty, \infty)$. Thus, an oriented abstract object A can be identified with the totality of input-output pairs which belong to A.

The members of the family $\{R_{[t_0, t_1]}\}$ are required to satisfy the consistency condition: If $(u_{[t_0, t_1]}, y_{[t_0, t_1]})$ is an input-output pair belonging to A, so is any section of this pair, i.e., any pair of the form $(u_{[\tau_0, \tau_1]}, y_{[\tau_0, \tau_1]})$ in which $t_0 \leq \tau_0 \leq t_1$, $\tau_0 \leq \tau_1 \leq t_1$, and $u_{[\tau_0, \tau_1]} = u_{[t_0, t_1]}$, $y_{[\tau_0, \tau_1]} = y_{[t_0, t_1]}$ over $[\tau_0, \tau_1]$. In plain words, this condition requires that every section of an input-output pair of A be in itself an input-output pair for A. The purpose of this condition is to ensure that the family $\{R_{[t_0, t_1]}\}$, $t_0, t_1 \in (-\infty, \infty)$, is defined in a consistent fashion.

The set of all segments u over $[t_0, t_1]$, such that $(u, y) \in A$, will be referred to as an *input segment space* of A and will be denoted by $R[u]$. Similarly, the set of all segments y, such that $(u, y) \in A$, will be referred to as an *output segment space* of A and will be denoted by $R[y]$. This implies that $R_{[t_0, t_1]}$, which is the set of all pairs $(u_{[t_0, t_1]}, y_{[t_0, t_1]})$ belonging to A, is a subset of the product space $R[u] \times R[y]$.

The crux of this definition is that it identifies an oriented abstract object with a "catalog" of ordered pairs (u, y) of segmented time functions defined in a consistent fashion on all subintervals of the real line. In this catalog, to a fixed u there corresponds, in general, a set of y's and, conversely, to a fixed y corresponds a set of u's.

From a mathematical point of view, what we have done amounts essentially to defining a system * as a *relation* rather than—as is more customary—a function or an operator. To illustrate this difference in view points, let us consider a very simple system such as an integrator. In this case, the (real-valued) input at time t, $u(t)$, and the (real-valued) output at time t, $y(t)$, are related to one another by the differential equation

$$\frac{d\,y(t)}{dt} = u(t) \tag{10}$$

Equivalently, we can say that an integrator is an oriented abstract object consisting of ordered pairs of time functions of the form $(u(t), \alpha + \int_{t_0}^{t} u(\xi)\,d\xi)$, $t_0 \leq t \leq t_1$, $t_0, t_1 \in (-\infty, \infty)$, in which α is a parameter ranging over the real line and u ranges over the class of time functions which are integrable over every finite interval. In this case, to each fixed $u_{[t_0,\ t_1]}$ corresponds a set of $y_{[t_0,\ t_1]}$ generated by the parameter α:

$$y(t) = \alpha + \int_{t_0}^{t} u(\xi)\,d\xi \qquad t_0 \leq t \leq t_1 \tag{11}$$

Any mathematical relation between u's and y's defining the totality of input-output pairs which constitute A is referred to as an *input-output relation* for A. In this sense, eq. 10 is an input-output relation for the integrator. Note that we do not regard the integrator in question as an operator, since an operator—by its definition—must associate a unique output time function to each input time function on which it operates. More generally, if the input and output of A satisfy a differential equation of the form

$$a_n(t)\frac{d^n y}{dt^n} + \cdots + a_0(t)y = b_m(t)\frac{d^m u}{dt^m} + \cdots + b_0(t) \tag{12}$$

then this equation constitutes an input-output relation for A because it defines the set of all input-output pairs belonging to A.†

So far nothing has been said about the state of A. To provide a justification for introducing it, we note that it would be convenient if

---

* The term "system" is used here in the same sense as an oriented abstract object. Actually, the notion of a system is somewhat broader than that of an oriented abstract object since a system need not be oriented. This point is discussed more fully in Ref. 9.

† It should be emphasized that here and elsewhere in this chapter we are not conducting our discussion on a high level of mathematical rigor. In the case of eq. 12, this manifests itself in our omission of any regularity conditions on the a's, b's, u's, and y's.

we could parametrize (or label) the set of input-output pairs $R_{[t_0, t_1]}$ in such a way that to each input segment $u_{[t_0, t_1]}$ and each value of the parameter (label) would correspond a unique output segment $y_{[t_0, t_1]}$. Roughly speaking, such a parametrization can be likened to numbering the pages of a catalog which lists the input-output pairs belonging to A. As we shall see presently, the states of A are essentially the values of the parameter in question.

From this point of view, the primary role of the notion of state is to provide a way of associating a unique output to each input, with the state serving as a parameter. A more detailed discussion of how this can be done is presented in the following section.

THE NOTION OF STATE

Let α be a parameter ranging over a space Σ. (Usually α is an n-vector and Σ is R^n, the space of ordered n-tuples of real numbers.) Let (u, y), where $u \overset{\Delta}{=} u_{(t_0, t_1]}$, $y \overset{\Delta}{=} y_{(t_0, t_1]}$,* be an input-output pair belonging to A. Then we shall say that α *parametrizes* A if there exists a function $\bar{A}$ on the product space $\Sigma \times R[u]$ such that for all (u, y) belonging to A and all t_0 and t, we can find an α in Σ such that

$$y = \bar{A}(\alpha; u) \tag{13}$$

Furthermore, for each α in Σ and each u in $R[u]$, the pair $(u, \bar{A}(\alpha: u))$ is an input-output pair belonging to A.

In plain terms, these conditions mean that every pair (u, y) which satisfies eq. 13 for some α in Σ is an input-output pair of A and, conversely, every input-output pair of A satisfies eq. 13 for some α in Σ.

The mere fact that α parametrizes A is not sufficient to justify calling α a state of A. In addition, $\bar{A}$ must have the response separation property stated below in definition 5.

As a preliminary to stating the response separation property, it will be helpful to agree on the following convention: A segment $u \overset{\Delta}{=} u_{(t_0, t]}$ followed by a segment $v \overset{\Delta}{=} v_{(t, t_1]}$ is denoted by uv. [This is one reason why we use semiclosed rather than closed observation intervals. If we used closed observation intervals, there would be a difficulty in defining the value of uv at t when $u(t) \neq v(t)$.] In particular, if $u \overset{\Delta}{=} u_{(t_0, t]}$ and $u' \overset{\Delta}{=} u_{(t, t_1]}$, then $uu' = u_{(t_0, t_1]}$.

* For reasons that will become clearer later, it is more appropriate to use semiclosed rather than closed observation intervals in this section.

Definition 5

The function $\bar{A}(\alpha; u)$ has the *response separation property* if for all α in Σ and all uu' in $R[uu']$ there exists an element α^* of Σ, with α^* uniquely determined by α and u, such that

$$\bar{A}(\alpha; uu') = \bar{A}(\alpha; u)\, \bar{A}(\alpha^*, u') \qquad (14)$$

In words, eq. 14 means that the output or, equivalently, the response segment corresponding to parameter α and to input segment uu' is identical with the response segment corresponding to α and u, followed by the response segment corresponding to α^* and u'.

The significance of the response separation property will become clearer once we have defined what is meant by the state of A. This is done in the following definition.

Definition 6

If α parametrizes A and $\bar{A}(\alpha; u)$ has the response separation property, then the elements of Σ constitute the *states* of A, Σ is the *state space* of A, and $y = \bar{A}(\alpha; u)$ is an *input-output-state relation* for A. If $u \stackrel{\Delta}{=} u_{(t_0, t]}$, then α in $\bar{A}(\alpha; u)$ is referred to as the *initial state* of A at time t_0, and is denoted by $s(t_0)$. Thus, the input-output-state relation may be written more explicitly as

$$y_{(t_0, t]} = \bar{A}(s(t_0); u_{(t_0, t]}) \qquad (15)$$

where $u_{(t_0, t]}$ is the input segment, $s(t_0)$ is the initial state, and $y_{(t_0, t]}$ is the corresponding response segment. In words, eq. 15 signifies that the initial state of A at time t_0 and the input segment $u_{(t_0, t]}$ uniquely determine the response segment $y_{(t_0, t]}$.

We have thus defined what is meant by the states of A and the initial state of A. Still unanswered is the question of what is meant by the state of A at time t. To define this notion, we can make use of the response separation property, eq. 14. Specifically, we have the following definition.

Definition 7

Suppose that A is initially in state $s(t_0) = \alpha$, and an input $u \stackrel{\Delta}{=} u_{(t_0, t]}$ is applied to A. By the response separation property, there exists an element $\alpha^* \in \Sigma$ such that eq. 14 holds for any $u \stackrel{\Delta}{=} u_{(t, t_1]}$. The element α^*, which is uniquely determined by $s(t_0)$ and $u_{(t_0, t]}$, is called the *state of A at time t* and is denoted by $s(t)$. Thus, the state of A at time t is uniquely determined by the state of A at time t_0 and by the values which the input takes between t_0 and t. In symbols, this is expressed by the relation

$$s(t) = s(s(t_0); u_{(t_0, t]})$$ (16)

which is called the *state equation* of A. Note that, in eq. 16, s is a function defined on the product space $\Sigma \times R[u]$. Note also that $s(s(t_0); u_{(t_0, t]})$ has the same significance as $\phi_u(t; t_0, x_0)$ in definition 2.

In terms of the symbols introduced above, the response separation property, eq. 14, may be expressed as

$$A(s(t_0); uu') = A(s(t_0); u) A(s(t); u')$$ (17)

In this form, it has a clearer intuitive meaning. Specifically, eq. 17 signifies that the response of A to uu' starting in state $s(t_0)$ is identical with the response of A to u starting in state $s(t_0)$, followed by the response of A to u' starting in state $s(t)$.

As shown in Ref. 9, if $\bar{A}(\alpha; u)$ has the response separation property of eq. 14 (or, equivalently, eq. 17), then the function s in eq. 16 has the *state separation property*

$$s(s(t_0); uu') = s(s(s(t_0); u); u')$$ (18)

This property is equivalent to the group property given by eq. 3, which we have encountered earlier in the definition of a dynamical system.

As a simple illustration, consider a system A characterized by the input-output relation

$$\frac{dy}{dt} + y = u$$ (19)

In this case, the input-output pairs over $(t_0, t_1]$ are of the form

$$(u(t), \alpha e^{-(t-t_0)} + \int_{t_0}^{t} e^{-(t-\xi)} u(\xi) \, d\xi) \qquad t_0 < t \leq t_1$$ (20)

If we identify Σ with the real line $(-\infty, \infty)$, then the variable α in eq. 20 parametrizes A. Furthermore, on writing

$$y(t) = \alpha e^{-(t-t_0)} + \int_{t_0}^{t} e^{-(t-\xi)} u(\xi) \, d\xi \qquad t_0 < t \leq t_1$$ (21)

it is easy to verify that the following identity holds:

$$\alpha e^{-(t-t_0)} + \int_{t_0}^{t} e^{-(t-\xi)} u(\xi) \, d\xi = \alpha^* e^{-(t-\tau)} + \int_{\tau}^{t} e^{-(t-\xi)} u(\xi) \, d\xi$$ (22)

where $t_0 < \tau \leq t$ and

$$\alpha^* = \alpha e^{-(\tau-t_0)} + \int_{t_0}^{\tau} e^{-(\tau-\xi)} u(\xi) \, d\xi$$ (23)

Equation 21 is equivalent to a relation of the form $y = \bar{A}(\alpha; u)$ (see eq. 13) since it yields the values of y for $t > t_0$. Furthermore, eqs. 22 and 23 imply that the right-hand member of eq. 21 has the response separation property. Consequently, eq. 21 qualifies to be called an input-output-state relation for A, with α being the state of A at time t_0 and $\Sigma = (-\infty, \infty)$. Note that, on setting $t = t_0$ (which is permissible if u has no delta functions at t_0), we obtain

$$s(t_0) = \alpha = y(t_0) \tag{24}$$

which shows that the state of A at time t_0 can be identified with the output of A at time t_0.

This concludes our definition and brief illustration of the notion of state. To summarize, the main features of this definition are the following.

1. The starting point of our definition is the concept of an oriented abstract object A, which is defined as a family of sets of ordered pairs of time functions. Under definition 3, an abstract object has an identity of its own, independent of the way in which a state description is associated with it.

2. The notion of state is introduced as a device to parametrize the set of input-output pairs in such a way as to achieve a unique dependence of the output on the input and state. Since, in general, there are many (indeed, infinitely many) ways in which the set of input-output pairs can be parametrized, the implication is that there are many (infinitely many) ways in which an input-output relation can be cast into the form of an input-output-state relation. Thus, in general, a given abstract object A can be associated with infinitely many input-output-state relations which, though distinct in form, are equivalent to one another. To put it another way, just as a matrix may be regarded as a representation of a linear operator in a particular coordinate system, so an input-output-state relation is a representation of an oriented abstract object for a particular mode of parametrization of its input-output pairs. This point is not made clear in the definition of a dynamical system, since the state is introduced into the description of the system at the outset.

3. Definition 3 defines a broader class of systems than the class of dynamical systems. Consequently, definitions 5 and 6 provide a more general definition of the concept of state than does the indirect definition that is implicit in the definition of a dynamical system.

We have not touched upon the numerous ramifications of the concept of state, nor have we discussed its applications in the analysis and synthesis of linear and nonlinear systems. For this, the reader is referred to Ref. 9 and to the voluminous literature on optimal control, dynamic programming, automata theory, and information theory.

REFERENCES

1. Poincare, H., "Sur les courbes definies par les equations differentielles," *J. Math. Pures et Appl.*, part 3, **1** (1885), pp. 167–244. Part 4, **2** (1886), pp. 151–217.
2. Birkhoff, G. D., "Dynamical Systems," *Amer. Math. Soc. Colloq. Publ.* (1927).
3. Markov, A. A., "Sur une proprieté génerale des ensembles minimaux de M. Birkhoff," *Comptes Rendus, Acad. Sci. Paris*, **193** (Nov. 1931), pp. 823–825.
4. Nemytskii, V. V., "Topological Questions in the Theory of Dynamical Systems," *Uspehi Mat. Nauk*, **4** (Nov.–Dec., 1949), pp. 91–153. *Amer. Math. Soc. Translation No. 103* (1954).
5. Pontryagin, L. S., and L. G. Shnierelman, "A General Investigation into Dynamical Systems," Unpublished Notes, Moscow University. (This work is cited by V. V. Nemytskii.)
6. Kalman, R., "Mathematical Description of Linear Dynamical Systems," *RIAS Technical Report 62–18* (Nov. 1962).
7. Gill, A., *Introduction to the Theory of Finite-State Machines*, McGraw-Hill Book Co., New York, 1962.
8. Ginsburg, S., *An Introduction to Mathematical Machine Theory*, Addison-Wesley Publ. Company, Reading, Mass., 1962.
9. Zadeh, L. A., and C. A. Desoer, *"Linear System Theory—The State Space Approach*, McGraw-Hill Book Co., New York, 1963.
10. Vogel, T., "Dynamique théorique et heredité," *Rend. del Seminario Mat. Univ. Torino*, **21** (April, 1962), pp. 87–98.

CHAPTER 4

GENERAL SYSTEM THEORY AND SYSTEMS RESEARCH: CONTRASTING CONCEPTIONS OF SYSTEMS SCIENCE

RUSSELL L. ACKOFF

I would like to contrast general systems theory and systems research with respect to several of their important characteristics. My assertions about general systems theory are based primarily on the writings of Bertalanffy, and my assertions about systems research are based on my own conception of operations research. Systems research includes a host of activities other than operations research, but I do think that operations research is typical of these with respect to the characteristics that I will consider. I do not mean to imply that all general systems theorists or systems or operations researchers would either accept or fit my characterizations.

I do not mean to imply that the two approaches to systems theory that I will discuss are the only ones. In a sense, I will draw attention only to two extremes, and there are many positions which lie between the two. Furthermore, my evaluative remarks about methodological implications of the two approaches do not imply that all the work falling in one camp is good and that falling in the other is bad. Good and bad work has been done in both camps. I am evaluating the methodological implications of "movements" taken holistically, not the individual researches of which these movements are made up.

Although I have a deep respect for much of the work done under the name of general systems theory, I am apprehensive about certain implications which Bertalanffy's conception of this theory has on possible unification of science. It will be recalled that he was largely motivated by a desire to unify science through general systems theory.

I will attempt to show that Bertalanffy tried to unify science by reassembling aspects of nature which science had already disassembled.

I shall argue that science can be unified without going through an initial disunification. Secondly, I shall try to show that Bertalanffy's method of unifying science would result in the further separation of both the theoretical and applied aspects of nonformal science, and of the formal and nonformal sciences.

Science refers both to an activity—the process of controlled inquiry —and to the product of that activity—a body of knowledge. It makes a difference, however, in which of these two ways one looks at science in attempting to unify it. General systems theory tends to look at science as a body of facts, laws, and theories. This is reflected in Kenneth Boulding's assertion [3] that "science is what can be talked about profitably by scientists in their role as scientists" (p. 198). The systems researcher, on the other hand, looks at science as an *activity*, and at knowledge as its product. To one, unification of science is a matter of concepts, symbols, and statements about phenomena; to the other, it is a matter of how scientific inquiry is conducted. According to Boulding: [3]

> The more science breaks into sub-groups . . . the less communication is possible among the disciplines, however, the greater chance there is that the total growth of knowledge is being slowed down by the loss of relevant communications. The spread of specialized deafness means that someone who ought to know something that someone else knows isn't able to find it out for lack of generalized ears.
>
> It is one of the main objectives of General System Theory to develop these generalized ears, and by developing a framework of general theory to enable one specialist to catch relevant communications from others (pp. 198–199).

Systems researchers, on the other hand, although usually trained as disciplinary specialists, work and communicate within multidisciplinary groups which seek to develop factual and general knowledge of systems, knowledge that does not lend itself to disciplinary classification. This knowledge provides a basis for more effective designs and operations of systems; i.e., it provides a technology as well as a science of systems.

Boulding distinguishes between *"hybrid disciplines"* which "come from respectable and honest academic parents" (e.g., social psychology and biochemistry) and *"multisexual interdisciplines"* which "have a much more varied and occasionally even obscure ancestry, and result from the reorganization of material from many different fields of study" [3] (p. 199). In the "multisexual interdiscipline," operations research, disciplinary material is *not* reorganized in the way Boulding describes because the subject matter of research is not disorganized into disciplinary material in the first place. Hence, contrary to what

Boulding suggests, operations researchers do not "pick out certain general phenomena which are found in many different disciplines, and seek to build up general theoretical models relevant to these phenomena" [3] (p. 200). Instead, they build up theory relevant to system phenomena taken holistically without regard to disciplinary divisions.

Bertalanffy [2] attempted to build a new structure for science over the ruins of the Unity of Science Movement initiated a few decades ago by the logical positivists. The logical positivists tried to unify science on the principle of conceptual *reductionism*. According to this principle, all scientific concepts are reducible to a set of ultimately irreducible concepts, which some thought were provided by direct observation and others thought of as undefined concepts of a formal system. Whatever their source, these concepts were identified as "physical thing predicates"; that is, physical properties of things. Since these conceptual elements out of which all other meaningful concepts are supposed to be derivable were thought to be physical attributes, physics assumed a position at the head of a hierarchy of scientific disciplines. Chemistry, biology, psychology, and social science then followed, in this order, each supposedly dealing with concepts which could be synthesized from those used by the "prior" disciplines. Hence, physics was taken to be the only discipline that was conceptually independent of other empirical sciences, and the dependence of the others was taken as one directional.

Science was not unified under the banner of conceptual reductionism for many reasons, only one of which I would like to consider herein. The logical positivists failed to understand that simplicity is not to be found at the beginning of inquiry, but, if at all, only at its end. Complex concepts are not built up out of simple ones; simple concepts are abstracted from complex ones. Hence, the logical positivists found themselves in the position of attempting to unify science by logically reconstructing science out of the pieces into which it had been disassembled.

Bertalanffy [2] did not reject the effort of the logical positivists on logical or methodological grounds, but on practical ones:

So far unification of science has been seen in the reduction of all sciences to physics, in the final resolution of all phenomena into physical events. This could be achieved, if ever, only in an inscrutable future (p. 306).

Hence, Bertalanffy did not perceive the fallacy of acquiring or reconstructing knowledge of the complex out of knowledge of the simple. Consequently, he fell prey to this fallacy in a much more subtle way than the logical positivists.

Bertalanffy accepted the current disciplinary structure of science as a starting point. By seeking structural isomorphisms among the laws established by the various scientific disciplines, he hoped to find a more general theory than could be produced by any one discipline. Hence, Bertalanffy implicitly assumed that the structure of nature is isomorphic with the structure of science. Nothing could be further from the truth. Nature is not disciplinary. The phenomena and the problems which nature presents to us are not divisible into disciplinary classes. We impose scientific disciplines on nature; it does not impose them on us. Some of the *questions* that we ask of nature—in contrast to the problems it presents to us—can be classified as physical, chemical, biological, and so on; but not the phenomena themselves. In order to construct a purely physical phenomenon (and it must be constructed), we must exclude from consideration a large number of nonphysical things present in the experience that contains the phenomenon. For example, automobile accidents can be viewed at least as physical, biological, psychological, sociological, and economic phenomena. To study them in any one of these ways is to exclude variables relevant from other points of view. One might accept this example but reject the generality it is supposed to illustrate. One might ask, for example, how the movements of the planets can be considered as anything but a physical phenomenon. Can one explain the difference between the Ptolemaic and Copernican concept of such motion on purely physical grounds? *Experience* of planetary motion is as much a biological, psychological, sociological, and economic phenomenon as it is physical. An experience always involves an observer as well as the observed, and this interaction is a legitimate area of inquiry to any discipline.

Therefore, posing the problem of unifying science by interrelating disciplinary output either in the form of facts or concepts (i.e., logical positivism), or laws or theories (i.e., general systems theory), is to try to lock the barn door after the horse has gone.

Now let us look at the intended product of general systems theory more closely. As an example of a general systems principle found by recognition of structural isomorphism, Bertalanffy[2] cited the exponential law:

. . . the exponential law applied to radioactive decay, to the breakdown of a chemical compound in monomolecular reaction, to the death of bacteria under the influence of light or disinfectants, to the consumption of an animal by starvation, and to the decrease of an animal or human population where death rate is higher than birth rate (p. 305).

Hans Jonas [5] commented on this specific illustration as follows:

A curve of the same general form describes the net result of quantitative changes occurring in both complexes. The only condition required for such a curve to result is that the continuous overall change is one in the number of its own agents and that its average rate per unit agent is constant. This condition can be fulfilled in an unlimited number of ways, from the snow ball rolling downhill to the multiplication rate of human inventions. For every given case, the applicability of the exponential law is a relevant fact, but is its concordance in that respect with other cases also a fact? It would be, if the holding of the same arithmetic relation were indicative of some common pattern of action whereby it is achieved, and were thus in some way characteristic for the ways or the order of Nature (p. 330).

C. G. Hempel [4] commented more generally on the value of disclosing structural isomorphisms in this way:

It does not seem to me . . . that the recognition of isomorphisms between laws adds to, or deepens, our theoretical understanding of the phenomenon in the two fields concerned; for such understanding is accomplished by subsuming the phenomena under general laws or theories; and the applicability of a certain set of theoretical principles to a given class of phenomena can be ascertained only by empirical research, not through pure system theory (p. 315).

Bertalanffy [2] replied to such criticism as follows:

A classical case of Gaussian distribution is the deviation of hits from the bull's eye of a target; on the other hand, a Gaussian curve applied—among innumerable other phenomena—to the distribution of phenotypes in the seemingly non-Mendelian heredity due to multiple factors, for example, length of ears in corn or other differences in size. This example corresponds in its logical structure to that given by Jonas. In the first case, an overall formula covers a directly observed phenomenon. In the second, hypothetical entities are assumed in order to explain an observed phenomenon. Following Jonas' line of argument, we would have to say: in inheritance based upon multiple factors, there is certainly no gun, gunner, or target; it would be nonsensical to apply such notions to the hypothetical substructure of heredity; that the same integral applies in both cases amounts to no more than that $2 + 2 = 4$; and statistics is bunk. Fortunately such a conclusion was not drawn, and so the question remains as to what is at the basis of isomorphy. The answer is, of course, that it is the concept of chance. In the case of the marksman, the shooting is influenced by a number of independent factors. In the case of multiple factors in heredity, the distribution of phenotypes results from the combination of a series of independent games that control a character such as size. Therefore, the binominal distribution will apply in both cases.

. . . Of course, the occurrence of identical mathematical expressions is not in itself a proof that the phenomena concerned are "homologous" system phenomena; all that is contended is that if systems are considered, certain general principles will apply to them (pp. 340–341).

I do not find this a very satisfactory reply. It is not necessary to observe the application of the Gaussian law in different disciplines to perceive that chance is involved. Consequently, what is learned from the observed isomorphism is not at all clear to me. In the latter part of his reply, Bertalanffy does seem to retreat to the argument that revelation of such isomorphism has heuristic value; that is, it may lead to the discovery of a system principle, but by itself it reveals nothing new about the structure or operation of systems.

It seems to me that systems research is on sounder ground than general systems theory because it takes systems as it finds them, i.e., holistically, in all their multidisciplinary glory. It unifies the disciplines in the conduct of research and, hence, it produces facts, laws, and theories which are multidisciplinary in character. The theories produced by operations research, for example, do more than summarize a set of available theories in a cross-disciplinary language because these theories come out of the study of systems rather than the study of theories of systems.

Consider, for example, the nature of inventory theory, a product of operations research. This theory is applicable to all open systems in which the exchange of material or energy (and hence information) with the system's environment is at least partially controllable. If increases in the rate of input are accompanied by an increase in at least one (well-defined) benefit and one (well-defined) loss, we have the conditions necessary for an inventory process.

The most familiar setting of inventory processes is in business and industry. A company may control the rate of input of raw material by manipulating purchase quantities or the frequency of purchase, or both. If the purchase (input) rate exceeds the output (e.g., sales) rate, an inventory results which normally involves a loss in the form of "holding costs" (e.g., costs of storage, insurance, taxes, spoilage, and obsolescence). On the other hand, large inventories may reduce the likelihood of running out of stock and the costs associated with shortages or delays, and large purchases may reduce both the unit price (through quantity discounts) and the setup cost of processing purchases.

The theory takes the form of equations which express the sum of the costs and/or benefits (the measure of performance, P) as a function of (a) the values of the controlled variables, C_i, and (b) the values of the uncontrolled variables, U_j, which characterize relevant properties of both the system itself and its environment; that is,

$$P = f(C_i, U_j)$$

If the values which the controlled variables can assume are subject to constraints, these are expressed in a set of supplementary equations or inequations; for example,

$$C_1 \geq 0$$

The equations which make up inventory theory range from the very general to the very particular. A complete generalization has not as yet been obtained, but rapid progress is being made in this direction. (An example of a very general formulation can be found in Arrow, Karlin, and Scarf.[1]) The less general equations are deducible from the more general ones, but were not necessarily discovered by deduction. Many were developed in particular researches and subsequently generalized. There has been a continuous interplay of empirical and theoretical researches in this area.

This type of theory may be used either (1) to predict future system performance, (2) to explain past performance, (3) to explore the sensitivity of system performance to values of the variables defining the system, or (4) to determine those values of the controlled variables which optimize system performance.

Within the industrial context, inventory theory can be applied to such diverse phenomena as the acquisition and use of operating capital, the hiring and training of personnel, and the determination of how much and how frequently to acquire productive capacity. It is also applicable to any type of input-output system to which benefits and losses can accrue. For example, the metabolic processes of a living organism can be studied as an inventory process, the operation of a heating system, a computing center, a documentation center, and the natural water system of a geographical region. The inputs, outputs, and system involved can be of relevance to any and every scientific discipline. The disciplinary characteristics of the relevant variables have no relevance to the theory.

Operations research has produced a number of other theories with similar characteristics; for example, allocation, queuing, sequencing, routing, replacement, competitive, and search theories. These theories provide *new* ways of studying phenomena holistically and are not restricted to finding structural similarities in old ways of looking at things.

The eight bodies of theory which are developing in operations research are neither exclusive nor exhaustive. Structural isomorphisms between several aspects of these have already been found, e.g., between game theory and linear allocation theory. Consequently, there is no doubt that higher order generalizations than have yet been obtained are forthcoming. Such generalizations will reveal more and more of the fundamental structure of organized systems.

I now turn to a second aspect of general systems theory. Bertalanffy [2] conceived of this theory as a pure formal science:

> General System Theory would be an exact doctrine of wholeness as a "pure natural science" . . . that is, it is a hypothetico-deductive system of those principles which follow from the definition of system and by the introduction of more or less special conditions. In this sense, system theory is *a priori* and independent of its interpretation in terms of empirical phenomena, but it is applicable to all empirical realms concerned with systems. Its position is similar to that, for example, of probability theory, which is itself a formal mathematical doctrine but which can be applied, by way of empirical interpretation of its terms, to different fields . . . (p. 304).

The comparison of general systems theory and probability theory is a misleading one. They may both be formal *a priori* theories but, whereas theories which are developed within disciplines are in no sense special cases or interpretations of probability theory, they were supposed by Bertalanffy to be deducible from general systems theory. Put another way, general systems theory would be a metatheory, a theory to explain disciplinary theories. Its validity would depend on the deducibility of disciplinary theories from it and, hence, in turn, on the validity of the disciplinary theories. It is thus twice removed from the experimental and applied aspects of science. Consequently, the development of the theory, on the one hand, and its application in systems research, on the other, tend to be even more separated than they are within the traditional scientific disciplines.

The theoretician within a discipline can at least take frequent excursions into the relevant experimental and applied area, but it does not seem likely that the general systems theorist can tour each discipline with sufficient frequency to keep the deductive and inductive aspects of science unified. It seems, therefore, that the breach between theory and experimentation and application would be increased, a breach that is already too wide within many disciplines. The general systems theorist seems to be placing himself in a position as detached from science as that of the philosopher of science. Standing in such a position, it is unlikely that he will either integrate science or be integrated within it.

Operations research, in contrast, is conceived and dedicated to the principle that both the deductive and inductive phases of inquiry into systems be conducted simultaneously by the same multidisciplinary team. It seeks to unify inductive and deductive procedures by putting them into continuous interaction on the research job. Hence, operations research projects generally produce both theoretical and empirical knowledge of systems. Its approach to the methodology of science is as holistic as is its approach to the subject matter of science.

To be sure, operations research does not do away with the need for disciplinary specialists any more than the presence of an architect does away with the need for mechanical, civil, and electrical engineers in the design of structures. On the one hand, operations researchers can point out deficiencies in specialized knowledge within and between the scientific disciplines. For example, it has had a considerable impact on mathematics, especially in the development of mathematical programming, to mention only one case. On the other hand, specialized advances within disciplines have opened up possibilities which could be exploited by operations researchers. To draw another example from mathematics, developments in graph theory are having a growing impact on the methods and scope of operations research.

My final point refers to the concept of a system used in general systems theory. Bertalanffy [2] defines a systems as "complexes of elements in interaction to which certain system laws can be applied" (p. 307). If we interpret the terms used in this definition in their usual sense, the definition excludes systems whose components are concepts; for example, logical, numerical, linguistic, philosophic, ethical, and religious systems. Conceptual systems include the output of formal science as well as that of many nonscientific disciplines. Conceptual systems may differ in significant ways from concrete systems, but are they any the less systems for it? In order to include such systems, a system should be defined more generally as a complex of *interrelated entities*, not interacting elements.

If system theory is to be completely general, it must take conceptual systems into account. My feeling is that the effort to find general principles that apply to both conceptual and concrete systems is one of the most promising aspects of system science. Not only may it close the gap between formal and nonformal sciences but it may also close the gap between science and the arts and humanities. Perhaps systems science can do more than unify science, it may be able to help unify culture. If it were to succeed in doing this, would the unification of civilization be far behind?

REFERENCES

1. Arrow, K. J., Karlin, Samuel, and Scarf, Herbert, *Studies in the Mathematical Theory of Inventory and Production.* Stanford University Press, Stanford, California, 1958.

2. Bertalanffy, L. von, "Problems of General System Theory," *Human Biology,* **23** (1951), pp. 302–312.

——, "Conclusion," *Human Biology,* **23** (1951), pp. 336–345.

3. Boulding, K. E., "General Systems Theory—The Skeleton of Science," *Management Science,* **2** (1956), pp. 197–208.

4. Hempel, C. G., "General System Theory and the Unity of Science," *Human Biology,* **23** (1951), pp. 313–322.

5. Jonas, Hans, "Comment on General System Theory," *Human Biology,* **23** (1951), pp. 328–335.

CHAPTER 5

CONSTRAINED EXTREMIZATION MODELS AND THEIR USE IN DEVELOPING SYSTEM MEASURES

ABRAHAM CHARNES

WILLIAM W. COOPER

Programming sticks upon the shoals
Of incommensurate multiple goals,
And where the tops are no one knows
When all our peaks become plateaus
The top is anything we think
When measuring makes the mountain shrink.

The upshot is, we cannot tailor
Policy by a single scalar,
Unless we know the priceless price
Of Honor, Justice, Pride, and Vice.
This means a crisis is arising
For simple-minded maximizing.

                                        K. B.

INTRODUCTION

This chapter is concerned with models of the form

$$\max z \equiv \sum_{j=1}^{n} c_j x_j$$

subject to

$$\sum_{j=1}^{n} a_{ij} x_j \leq b_i \qquad i = 1, \cdots, m \tag{1}$$

$$x_j \geq 0 \qquad j = 1, \cdots, n$$

in order to secure the sharpness that linear programming lends to an analysis. Via this route we will then be able to sketch certain general ideas by means of a development that will proceed with reference to special artifacts for securing extensions for constrained optimization models, as they might be used for certain problems of system design. In this way we will then be in a better position to consider ways in which optimizations (extremal principles) might be used for purposes such as generating "equivalences" to do things like (a) obtaining suitable measures for assessing the performance of a system and (b) guiding and controlling certain kinds of simulation for system design purposes.*

The discussion centers about examples in management planning where these measures are used for evaluating design proposals. In such a context, the proposals are generally evaluated by reference to optimum performance.† But, of course, various artifacts make it possible also to utilize constrained extremization models for systems wherein optimization *per se* is not an issue. Such models may also be used in additional ways when, for instance, further evaluations are wanted to guide additional alterations in a system by reference to by-product information induced by an optimization principle. Of course, when artifacts have been employed—and the optimization itself may be such an artifact—then it may also be necessary to proceed with caution before utilizing such ancillary information.‡

A SLACK EQUIVALENT AND SOME TERMINOLOGY

For convenience of discussion, we now introduce certain terminology by reference to the following example, which is entirely equivalent to eq. 1,

$$\max z \equiv \sum_{j=1}^{n} c_j x_j$$

subject to

$$\sum_{j=1}^{n} a_{ij}x_j + y_i = b_i \qquad x_j, y_i \geq 0 \qquad (2)$$

$$i = 1, \cdots, m \qquad j = 1, \cdots, n$$

Here the y_i are called slack variables, and each such variable is positioned in a constraint formed from the structural variables x_j and structural coefficients a_{ij}, which are the same as in eq. 1, so that $y_i > 0$ means that $\Sigma a_{ij}x_j < b_i$ applies in both eqs. 2 and 1. The constant b_i in each such

* See Ref. 3 for examples of further artifacts that may be employed with linear programming algorithms.

† Notice, for instance, that the definition of economic (opportunity or alternative) cost is, in fact, defined in this way.

‡ See concluding section of this paper for further discussion.

expression is called a stipulation, and the scalar variable z provides a "figure of merit" generated by means of linear combinations of the criterion elements c_j and any program values x_j which may be assigned to the structural variables that appear in the functionals * for eqs. 1 and 2. Finally, the instruction "maximize z" will be called the objective. Thus, by reference to a resulting value for the figure of merit z, any program can be judged relative to other program possibilities and to the objective "maximize z."

DUALITY RELATIONS

Sometimes a model in the form of eq. 1 is referred to as a "direct" or "primal" linear programming problem to distinguish it from a related "dual problem" that can be formed from the same data—*viz.*,

$$\min g \equiv \sum_{i=1}^{m} w_i b_i$$

subject to

$$\sum_{i=1}^{m} w_i a_{ij} \geq c_j \qquad w_i \geq 0 \tag{3}$$

$$j = 1, \cdots, n \qquad i = 1, \cdots, m$$

When examining this dual problem, we may observe that a new objective is formed relative to a new figure of merit g. We also observe that exactly the same data are used in eqs. 3 and 1, with the following differences: (a) The structural coefficients are transposed when proceeding from one model to the other; (b) the inequalities are reversed for the structural constraints; and (c) the stipulations of one problem become the criterion elements for its dual correspond and *vice versa*. Finally, we observe that

$$\min g \equiv \sum_{i=1}^{m} w_i b_i$$

subject to

$$\sum_{i=1}^{m} w_i a_{ij} - u_j = c_j \qquad w_i, u_j \geq 0 \tag{4}$$

$$i = 1, \cdots, m \qquad j = 1, \cdots, n$$

is a slack equivalent to eq. 3 in much the same way that eq. 2 is a slack equivalent for eq. 1.

* The terms "functional" and "function" will be used interchangeably.

The properties of duality in linear programming [9a] have been the subject of a great deal of study, and are often put to use for such purposes as establishing or deriving model equivalences as well as controlling or bounding solutions when approximations are being utilized or when recourse is made to one problem in lieu of the other —e.g., for the purpose of reducing the number of computations—by reference, say, to the number or kinds of constraints which appear in a direct- and dual-problem pair.

Duality and Some System Evaluation Measures

The theory of duality which relates eqs. 1 and 3 may itself be used for system evaluation purposes. Some aspects of this may be illustrated by the relations

$$\sum_{j=1}^{n} c_j x_j \equiv z \leq g \equiv \sum_{i=1}^{m} w_i b_i \qquad (5)$$

which must hold between *any* set of x_j and w_i values that satisfy the constraints of eqs. 1 and 3. Furthermore, if both problems have solutions, then z^* and g^* will be optimal figures of merit if and only if

$$z^* = g^* \qquad (6)$$

One of the ways in which eq. 5 might be used is as follows: Consider any *given* problem, such as eq. 1, and suppose that a set of w_i values is somehow available which satisfies eq. 3.* With these w_i values, however, we can readily employ the definition $\Sigma w_i b_i \equiv g$ and utilize eq. 5 to secure an upper bound, $g \geq z$, for the latter figure of merit which may be the one that is actually of interest. If, also, a set of x_j values satisfying eq. 1 is available which results in a value $g - z = \delta > 0$, we know, by eq. 6, that this program is not optimal but, nevertheless, we may cease further computations if δ is small enough. Furthermore we may, if we desire, regard $\delta > 0$ as a suitable scalar measure of deviation in system performance in the sense that it provides an upper bound † to the amount of deviation that is possible.

The relation of eq. 6, which is sharper than eq. 5, can sometimes be used to obtain a set of system measures. One way for doing this may be illustrated as follows. Suppose it is desired to alter some of the stipulations b_i for a problem in the form of eq. 1 after an optimum set

---

* For example, because the algorithm which is being utilized makes these values available. See, e.g., Chapters XIII and XIV in Ref. 3 for a discussion of "subdual algorithms" which can sometimes be employed for these purposes.

† Indeed, an optimizing g^* value provides a least upper bound for this purpose when it is available.

of program values x_j* has been obtained and deemed to be not wholly satisfactory for the reason that, say, the figure of merit resulting from these program values is not sufficiently good. Then, suppose it is also known * that some subset of the w_i* values will remain constant over some prescribed set of variations that are to be examined, relative to the initial b_i stipulations, in order to study ways to improve the figure of merit for the direct problem. Now observe that the stipulations for eq. 3 are composed from the criterion elements of eq. 1 which are not being disturbed here. Thus, if we decompose the indices i into subsets I_1 and I_2, according to whether the associated b_i is being varied, we can then utilize the previously achieved w_i* values and write

$$\hat{g} \equiv \sum_{i \in I_1} w_i^*(b_i + \Delta b_i) + \sum_{i \in I_2} w_i^* b_i \qquad (7)$$

The resulting $\hat{g}$ value is optimal for a new dual problem which has, by way of its altered functional elements, a new direct problem of the form

$$\max \tilde{z} \equiv \sum_{j=1}^{n} c_j \tilde{x}_j$$

subject to

$$\sum_{j=1}^{n} a_{ij} \tilde{x}_j \leq b_i + \Delta b_i \qquad i \in I_1$$

$$\sum_{j=1}^{n} a_{ij} \tilde{x}_j \leq b_i \qquad i \in I_2 \qquad (8)$$

$$x_j \geq 0 \qquad j = 1, \cdots, n$$

in which the stipulations with indices $i \in I_1$ are altered. Now noticing that our attention is directed only toward examining figure-of-merit variations, we can go one step further when we do not wish to be encumbered with the need for determining the $\tilde{x}_j$ values that will be used to produce an optimal $\tilde{z}$ value. In fact, relation 6 permits us to do this since, if $\hat{z}$ is an optimal figure of merit for eq. 8, we know, through eq. 6, that we must have $\hat{g} = \hat{z}$, and so we can confine ourselves only to examining the single relation (eq. 7) in lieu of examining the generally more complex system.

Of course, in many cases we may want to elect alternative courses under which we can, in advance, prescribe a minimum level of improvement for z* and permit other data variations in addition to stipulation alterations of the kind we have been examining. A discussion of how this can be done will be essayed in the next section. In preparation for

---

* This knowledge is readily available from most of the computer codes now used on linear programming problems.

later sections, however, we should now note that the optimal dual variables w_i^* are sometimes referred to as "evaluators" and, in fact, it is sometimes useful to consider all of them as elements of a set of measures for evaluating alterations or operations in different parts of a total system.

An easy way, perhaps, to approach the latter topic is to regard all of these w_i^* values in a manner analogous to the way in which pricing systems are supposed to perform in the theory of market economics. In fact, these dual evaluators can actually be characterized precisely in this way for the purpose of studying certain kinds of market economies or for studying their possible value in guiding the operations of a decentralized firm. One way for doing this, as suggested by T. C. Koopmans,[9b] may be summarized, very roughly, as follows.* Let the x_j variables be referred to as activity levels, and let each vector of a_{ij} values that is associated with an x_j variable be referred to as an activity vector. These activity vectors are formed from the columns of the a_{ij} data and then distinguished from the corresponding row vectors which can also be formed from these same arrays of a_{ij} data; the row vectors are referred to as commodity vectors. Each commodity vector is then placed under the charge of a person referred to as a "custodian." Each activity is placed under a "manager." Each custodian knows only the data (including the stipulation) in his own row. Each manager knows only the data in his own column.

But now observe that this manager-and-custodian characterization conforms in a general way to the data transpositions which are effected when moving from one linear programming problem to its dual. Thus, by assuming this possibly extreme state of ignorance, these direct-dual-problem relations may be called upon to generate information devices— in the nature of costs and prices †—which enable separate parts of a system to work together in a coordinated way to obtain certain over-all organization objectives (even though the independent parts are not motivated by these particular objectives, *per se*, and, indeed, may be wholly ignorant of them). In some cases, e.g., for business firms, this over-all objective may be defined relative to a single scalar (figure of merit) such as maximum profit. In other cases, e.g., an economic system, it may be necessary, or desirable, to utilize a whole set of measures to characterize, say, the amount of consumer welfare obtainable from the system. For either case, however, it is possible to consider the

---

* See also Ref. 10 and Chapter IX and Appendix D in Ref. 3 for further discussion and extensions.

† Sometimes called "shadow costs" or "transfer prices" to distinguish them from other related data such as are contained in cost reports, market reports, etc. See Refs. 9b and 10, also Chapter IX in Ref. 3.

problem from a linear (or nonlinear) programming standpoint, and then to delineate a dual problem with associated variables whose values, interpreted as "prices," provide the necessary information theoretic content for the coordination to be achieved without disturbing the degree of decentralization being utilized.

SOME SCALARS FOR MEASURING AND EVALUATING SYSTEMS *

We now consider some aspects of "model equivalence" in a way that will (a) cast further light on possible uses for constrained extremization models in system redesigns and (b) extend our previous discussion of the stipulation alterations that were examined relative to eqs. 1 and 8. For concreteness, we shall suppose that the data of eq. 1 again apply and that we have solved the problem as it was initially stated in eq. 1. This means, of course, that we also know the optimal z^*.

Supposing that this known figure of merit is again deemed to be unsatisfactory, we now wish to consider a more general model in which alterations will be permitted in the original structural coefficients a_{ij} as well as in the original stipulations b_i. For this purpose we introduce the model

$$\max \hat{z} \equiv \sum_{j=1}^{n} c_j x_j - \mathcal{C}_1(\cdots \epsilon_{ij}x_j \cdots) - \mathcal{C}_2(\cdots y_i \cdots)$$

subject to

$$\sum_{j=1}^{n} (a_{ij} - \epsilon_{ij})x_j \leq b_i + y_i \qquad (9)$$

$$\epsilon_{ij}x_j \leq \bar{\epsilon}_{ij}x_j \qquad y_i \leq d_i$$

$$-\sum_{j=1}^{n} c_j x_j + \mathcal{C}_1(\cdots \epsilon_{ij}x_j \cdots)$$

$$+ \mathcal{C}_2(\cdots y_i \cdots) \leq -z^*(1 + \mathcal{K}) \qquad x_j, y_i \geq 0$$

As already observed, z^* is known and $\mathcal{K}$ is a positive constant (also known), so that $z^*(1 + \mathcal{K})$, which serves as a stipulation for the last constraint, requires that we obtain an increment of at least $\mathcal{K}z^*$ in our new figure of merit. Of course, the criterion elements c_j (like the a_{ij}) are known constants which have the same values in both eqs. 1 and 2. The ϵ_{ij} are variables, however, and so we now admit the possibility of altering the structural coefficients to new values $\tilde{a}_{ij} = (a_{ij} - \epsilon_{ij})$. Similarly,

* The materials in this section are drawn from Ref. 4.

we have the possibility of altering the original b_i stipulations to new values $\tilde{b}_i = b_i + y_i$. The latter alterations are confined by the d_i stipulations supplied in the form of known constants, so that $y_i \leq d_i$ limits the alterations which are permitted. The structural alterations, on the other hand, are confined by the looser $\epsilon_{ij} x_j \leq \tilde{\epsilon}_{ij} x_j$, with the $\tilde{\epsilon}_{ij}$ representing specified constants (possibly zero) for each i and j.

The functions $\mathcal{C}_1(\cdots \epsilon_{ij} x_j \cdots)$ and $\mathcal{C}_2(\cdots y_i \cdots)$, which appear in the last constraint and also in the functional,* represent the cost of securing the indicated improvements, and these are both assumed to be convex functions of their arguments and, for most managerial problems, these $\mathcal{C}_1$ and $\mathcal{C}_2$ functions will be strictly increasing as well as convex.

It may help now to interpret eq. 9 in terms of a problem in production management wherein an optimum is to be attained which simultaneously determines (a) the best improvements in the structural coefficients for the processes that are being utilized, (b) the capacity alterations which should also be undertaken and, finally, (c) the best current levels and mixes of outputs and inputs.

If finite optimum values can be secured which are positive, then we can write

$$\max \tilde{z} = \tilde{z}^* \geq z^*(1 + \mathcal{K}) > z^* = \max z \tag{10}$$

wherein z^* refers to eq. 9, the new problem, and z^* refers to the old one, eq. 1. Evidently, then, z^* and $\tilde{z}^*$ as well as $\delta^* = \tilde{z}^* - z^* > 0$ are all available as scalar measures to evaluate each system and the related alterations which can be undertaken at an optimum in each case.

We now introduce,

$$\max \hat{z} \equiv \sum_k \hat{c}_k \hat{x}_k$$

subject to

$$\sum_k \hat{a}_{rk} \hat{x}_k \leq \hat{b}_r \qquad \hat{x}_k \geq 0, \text{ all } k \tag{11}$$

as another linear programming model in order to elucidate certain ideas which we shall refer to as "repricing," "reprocessing," and "restructuring." We also suppose that certain known relations are available, viz.,

$$x_j = f_j(\cdots, \hat{x}_k, \cdots)$$
$$y_i = \phi_i(\cdots, \hat{x}_k, \cdots) \tag{12}$$
$$\epsilon_{ij} = \psi_{ij}(\cdots, \hat{x}_k, \cdots)$$
$$i = 1, \cdots, m \qquad j = 1, \cdots, n$$

* This makes this model a problem in "goal programming," as discussed in Appendix B ff. of Ref. 3.

with, in particular, $x_j{}^* = f_j(\cdots, \hat{x}_k{}^*, \cdots)$, so that, when an optimum is available from eq. 11, it can be inserted into eq. 12 to produce an optimum for eq. 9 as well.*

Motivation for the terms "repricing," "reprocessing," etc., can be secured by observing that eq. 11 is the same as the original problem, eq. 1, except that new data are employed for its criterion elements, structural coefficients, and stipulations. Thus, if the number of variables and constraints are the same in these two models and if $\hat{b}_i = b_i$ and $\hat{a}_{ij} = a_{ij}$ all i, j, but if, for arbitrary j, we *cannot* assert $\hat{c}_j = c_j$, then we may say that eq. 11 is a "repriced" version of the original model. Alternatively, if for some i and j we have $\hat{a}_{ij} \neq a_{ij}$ or $\hat{b}_i \neq b_i$, then we may refer to eq. 11 as a "reprocessed model" when only $\hat{c}_j = c_j$ all j. Finally, if the number of constraints and variables are altered but eqs. 1 and 11 are otherwise both represented in the same general form, then we shall say that a "restructuring" has occurred.

In general, if we can specify a procedure which shows how to effect the indicated data alterations so that, by way of eq. 12, we have an equivalence between eqs. 11 and 9, then we say that we have established a "repricing theorem," a "reprocessing theorem," or a "restructuring theorem," or such combinations of these theorems as the applicable instance may require.

If $\mathcal{C}_1$ and $\mathcal{C}_2$ are piecewise linear, then, as we have elsewhere shown,[1] such theorems may be used to produce a repriced, reprocessed, and restructured version of eq. 9 in the form

$$\max \sum_{j \neq q} c_j \hat{x}_j + \sum_q \left(c_q - \sum_p c_{pq} \bar{a}_{pq} \right) \hat{x}_q - \sum_i c_i \hat{y}_i$$

subject to

$$\sum_{j=q} a_{ij} \hat{x}_j - \hat{y}_i \leq b_i \qquad i \neq p \tag{13}$$

$$\sum_q (a_{pq} - \bar{a}_{pq}) \hat{x}_q - \hat{y}_p \leq b_p$$

$$\hat{x}_j, \hat{x}_q, \hat{y}_p, \hat{y}_i \geq 0$$

wherein eqs. 12 assume the very simple form

$$x_j{}^* = \hat{x}_j{}^*$$

$$y_i{}^* = \hat{y}_i{}^*$$

$$y_{ij} \equiv \epsilon_{ij} x_j \tag{14}$$

$$\bar{a}_{ij} \equiv \bar{\epsilon}_{ij}$$

and $\bar{\epsilon}_{ij} \equiv 0$ except for $i = p$ and $j = q$.

---

* Or at least it must be possible to identify solutions for the new model which can then be used to generate the wanted optimal values for eq. 9.

It should be emphasized, perhaps, that "equivalences" between optimization models need only be established for the optimal programs. Indeed, it need not even be the case that the figures of merit must achieve the same value for an equivalent pair. Notice, for instance, that an optimum $\hat{z}^*$ for eq. 11 need not be the same as an optimum $\bar{z}^*$ for eq. 9.

Equations 14 are of a very simple kind but, of course, more complex relations must generally be expected. However, so long as eqs. 12 are known, there is no great trouble so far as these scalars are concerned since a simple substitution in the functional for eq. 9 produces the correct z^*. The matter may be more serious, however, when component evaluations are wanted. The problem of eq. 11, for instance, has a corresponding dual, but the associated w_i^* "evaluators" cannot always be applied for altering the b_i of eq. 11 without first according them further treatment. Evidently the eqs. 12 must also be considered for this purpose and, perhaps, altered further when parametric variations of the a_{ij}, b_i, d_i or ϵ_{ij} values are of interest.

SOME VECTOR MEASURES OF SYSTEM EFFICIENCY

We have already mentioned situations in which it may be necessary (or desirable) to synthesize a set (or vector) of measures for evaluating a system. Since the preceding (scalar measure) case was developed by reference to examples where optimizations were directly involved, it may now be well to illustrate a situation in which such an optimization is used only as an artifact.

For this purpose we now introduce matrix notation and embed all of the relevant structural data in a matrix (of suitable order) symbolized as A. Following the terminology of T. C. Koopmans,[9b] we can refer to A as a "technology matrix" of known constants. We also associate with A a vector of activity (decision) variables which we symbolize by x; then we write

$$Ax = y$$
$$x \geq 0$$

(15)

to mean that, when any set of x values is applied to the "technology" A, then a set of values is generated for a corresponding "commodity vector" * y, wherein are impounded all inputs and outputs for the system. Still following Koopmans, we distinguish a subset of these

---

* The term "commodity" is to be regarded as having mainly generic significance and can refer to services as well as goods.

y values as "final commodities" which are symbolized y_F and confined by the condition $y_F \geqq 0$ because they are the "goods" which are "wanted" as final outputs. Another subset of the vector y, symbolized y_P, represents "primary commodities" which serve as initial inputs to the system. Via the conventions used in such analyses, these inputs are usually associated with a negative sign and confined by constraints of the form $-y_P \leqq -\eta_P$, where $\eta_P \leqq 0$ is a vector of stipulations which limits the amount of each input that is available. Finally, the remaining possibility in y is a set of so-called intermediate commodities which are internal to the system (e.g., transfer of products from one machine or service station to another), and these are symbolized by y_I and constrained by the condition $y_I = 0$.

Although Koopmans' analyses proceed directly by reference to these y_F, y_P, and y_I variables * for characterizations of system "efficiency," pricing considerations, etc., we shall want to proceed more generally by reference to what we have elsewhere called "functional efficiency" † as contrasted with the simpler "K efficiency" ‡ that Koopmans utilizes. For this we introduce the vector of functionals defined by

$$
f(y_F) \equiv
\begin{bmatrix}
f_1(y_F) \\
f_2(y_F) \\
\cdots\cdots \\
f_j(y_F) \\
\cdots\cdots \\
f_k(y_F)
\end{bmatrix}
\tag{16}
$$

so that the vector of final goods y_F enters into the arguments of f as well as each of its component functions $f_j(y_F)$, $j = 1, \cdots, k$.§ Then

* We should perhaps note that this decomposition of y is assumed to be mutually exclusive and collectively exhaustive. This is not so confining as might be supposed, however, since a variety of artifacts may be used in cases where a particular good or service is to be treated in more than one of the classifications.[9b, 10]

† See Chapter IX in Ref. 3 from which this and the remaining materials in this section are drawn.

‡ The K is in honor of Koopmans but, of course, these ideas are also related to such constructs as *Pareto optimality*, etc. See Chapter IX in Ref. 3.

§ The case in which some of the $f_j(y_F)$ functions are independent of particular final commodities is, of course, embraced in this formulation. See, e.g., Appendix D in Ref. 3.

we introduce the idea of functional efficiency in accordance with the following:

Definition (functional efficiency or f_j-efficiency): * $\hat{y}_F$ is "f_j-efficient" if and only if, for any y_F, $f_j(y_F) \geq f_j(\hat{y}_F) = > f_j(y_F) = f_j(\hat{y}_F)$, $j = 1$, 2, $\cdots$, k.

To see what is intended by this definition, let it be supposed that each $f_j(y_F)$ is a utility function which measures the satisfactions accorded to some consumer from any y_F that the system is capable of producing. These utility functions are ordinarily assumed to involve incommensurables. In particular, without further, somewhat arbitrary, assumptions, they cannot be associated with objective measures for comparing the satisfactions that different consumers might receive from different bills of final goods, y_F, which the system might be used to generate. On the other hand, at least under certain conditions, it is possible to "order" the satisfactions that each consumer might receive. Thus, when presented with a choice between two different vectors $\hat{y}_F$ and y_F, say, a particular consumer—the jth one, for instance—may be able to tell whether he prefers one to the other. Thus, if he prefers y_F to $\hat{y}_F$ or is indifferent to these choices, we can write $f_j(y_F) \geq f_j(\hat{y}_F)$, and if the opposite preference holds, we can write $f_j(y_F) < f_j(\hat{y}_F)$ even when we cannot assign a numerical measure to the resulting difference in any wholly satisfactory way.

When constrained optimizations are being employed, it is useful to distinguish these kinds of cases from those in which supposedly multiple goals can readily be accommodated in the constraints. For instance, business managements are sometimes said to be interested in things like employment stability, market penetration, etc., as well as in the objective of profit maximization. But conditions such as these can often be incorporated in the constraints—or perhaps treated by other artifacts —in which event they are not really multiple goals. Notice, for instance, that, if a market penetration constraint is incorporated in a linear programming model that is directed towards maximizing profits, then the marketing stipulation will appear as part of the objective in the associated dual problem. This means, in particular, that this stipulation admits of evaluations, and thus it is possible to secure comparisons between this supposedly additional goal and the direct profit maximizing objective.†

The incommensurabilities discussed in the aforementioned consumer

---

* The symbol " = >" means "implies that."

† This same comment applies to those situations in which "long-run profits" are supposed to act as a goal in addition to "short-run profits."

illustration cannot generally be compared in this simple way, and thus in any optimization we are permitted to compare different y_F vectors relative to each $f_j(y_F)$ in its own terms only. This has, of course, supplied a motivation for the above definition. Thus, consider a case opposite to the one included in the definition. A vector $\hat{y}_F$ is presented. However, after considering all production possibilities admitted by the model, we are able to discover another vector y_F which satisfies $f_j(y_F) \geq f_j(\hat{y}_F)$, all j, which means that no consumer will be worse off. We can, of course, always find such a vector by merely choosing $y_F = \hat{y}_F$. If, however, we find a $y_F \neq \hat{y}_F$ which satisfies $f_j(y_F) \geq f_j(\hat{y}_F)$, which means, as already observed, that no consumer will be worse off, and if, additionally, this does *not* imply $f_j(y_F) = f_j(\hat{y}_F)$, $j = 1, \cdots, k$ then it must be the case that $f_j(y_F) > f_j(\hat{y}_F)$ for some j. Hence, at least one consumer's satisfactions will be increased and no consumer will have his satisfactions worsened when y_F is designated for production in place of $\hat{y}_F$. Therefore, as the definition states, $\hat{y}_F$ would not be efficient and our definition suggests that the associated system measure must reveal that other y_F values are better.

There remains now the task of erecting a model that can be used for conducting the efficiency examinations that are wanted. For this purpose, we first decompose the technology matrix A into the submatrices A_F, A_I, and A_P, which are associated, respectively, with the divisions of y into y_F, y_I, and y_P, Then we write

$$\max e'_{\mathfrak{z}F}$$

subject to

$$A_F x - y_F = 0$$

$$A_I x = 0$$

$$A_P x - y_P = 0$$

$$y_P \geq \eta_P \tag{17}$$

$$f(y_F) - \mathfrak{z}_F = f(\hat{y}_F)$$

$$x, \mathfrak{z}_F \geq 0$$

Here the only new elements are the vector of nonnegative variables $\mathfrak{z}_F$, which has the same number of components as $f(y_F)$ (see eq. 16), and the row vector $e' = (1, 1, \cdots, 1)$. Evidently, then, our maximization is undertaken relative to $e'_{\mathfrak{z}F} \equiv \sum_{j=1}^{k} \mathfrak{z}_{Fj}$. But it is to be emphasized that this is only an artifact which we use by reason of the following:

Theorem: $\hat{y}_F$ is f_j-efficient if and only max $e'_{\mathfrak{z}F} = 0$.

The conditions $f(y_F) - \mathfrak{z}_F = f(\hat{y}_F)$ and $\mathfrak{z}_F \geq 0$ evidently prevent the emergence of any activity choices and resulting y_F values which will produce $f(y_F) < f(\hat{y}_F)$. On the other hand, if $e'\mathfrak{z}_F > 0$, it must be the case that $f_j(y_F) > f_j(\hat{y}_F)$ for some j, and in all other cases $f_r(y_F) \geq f_r(\hat{y}_F)$. From this we can conclude that $\hat{y}_F$ is not efficient and, furthermore, the resulting y_F may be utilized if an efficient vector is wanted. No discrimination is provided, however, between any pair of vectors that attain the status of efficiency. Furthermore, it is not even possible, generally, to compare two different y_F vectors, by virtue of the fact that one of them is associated with a greater or smaller functional value. That is, since vector comparisons are at issue, in this optimization, it is possible to obtain evaluations only by comparing like components and this, in turn, means that only a partial ordering is possible.

Unless the $f_j(y_F)$ functionals are suitably restricted, there will, in general, be no dual theorem that is applicable. Then no dual evaluators—and hence no prices—will be available either.

In some cases it is desirable to consider suitable ways of pricing, relative to the individual $f_j(y_F)$ functionals, in order to ensure that certain over-all goals are also secured as each $f_j(y_F)$ maximization is being undertaken. A case in point would be the use of departmental profit centers in a decentralized entity when, additionally, the pursuit of profits at each center is supposed (a) to produce an over-all maximum profit for the entire firm and (b) to conform to certain over-all constraints.* It is evident, however, that this cannot always be arranged unless the supposedly objective market data are adjusted along lines that were discussed previously in connection with our repricing and reprocessing theorems. Thus, if some departments can produce and sell at a profit only if others produce and sell at a loss,† then it may be necesary to devise artificial prices for the latter (and possibly the former) to respond to.

These kinds of topics have been treated elsewhere ‡ and so we shall not repeat them here. Our main point has been to illustrate how suitable vector measures of system performance can be secured even when multiple and incommensurable goals are involved. For the moment we can regard our definition of f_j efficiency and our model (eq. 17) as satisfactory for this purpose. In a subsequent section we can then turn to a problem of system evaluation which is, perhaps,

---

* For example, relative to certain additional "goals" such as market penetration, long-run growth, etc.

† A case in point is supplied by the so-called loss leaders that are often used in department store sales.

‡ See, e.g., Chapter IX and Appendix D in Ref. 3.

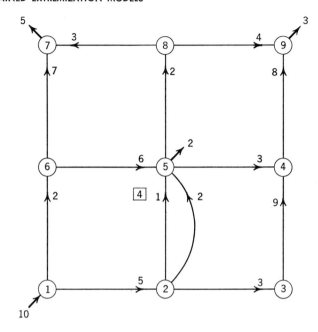

FIG. 1. Single-source network copy. (*Source:* Ref. 2, p. 642.)

less extreme in its requirements. This will be done after certain pre-liminaries are attended to in the next section.

ALGORITHMIC COMPLETION OF A LITERAL MODEL *

The example of Fig. 1 will now be used to illustrate the topic of this section as well as to introduce some of the material for the next section. This figure may be thought of as a network diagram in which the branches represent streets and the nodes represent possible points of origin or destination for traffic which is to flow over this system. Thus, in this interpretation, the heavy, inward-pointing arrow at node ① is intended to symbolize that ten vehicles are to be entered into the system at this point. The heavy, outward-pointing arrows at nodes ⑤, ⑦, and ⑨ are intended to mean that quantities of two, five, and three vehicles have their destinations, respectively, at these nodes.

For our immediate purposes, we may imagine that these data are being used by a truck despatcher whose objective is to schedule the

* The materials in this section are adapted from Chapter XVII in Ref. 3.

routings for these ten trucks in a way that will minimize the total number of vehicle hours required to fulfill their destination requirements. For this, of course, he will need the transit times likely to be experienced on the routes available to him.* These are supplied by the numbers positioned alongside the arrowheads. Thus, for instance, if the despatcher were to route two vehicles via the branches 1–2 and 2–5, then he would expect a result in vehicle hours in the amounts 2 × 5 (from 1–2) plus 2 × 1 (from 2–5) for a total of twelve vehicle hours.

The two links between nodes ② and ⑤ are intended to reflect a nonlinearity in that a transit time of 1 hour on this link is obtainable only when four or less vehicles are assigned to it. (See the ⎡4⎤ opposite the straight-line link connecting nodes ① and ②.) If more than four vehicles are assigned to this link, then the transit times will be increased as a function of the number of vehicles. To illustrate how this is to be handled, we may suppose, first, that five vehicles are assigned to this link. By the approximating fiction we are now using,† the transit time is to be increased from 1 hour per vehicle to $1\frac{1}{5}$ hours per vehicle in accordance with the expression $(4 + \Delta 2)/(4 + \Delta) = \frac{6}{5}$. That is, for the purpose of computing *total* transit times, four vehicles are considered to experience a one-hour transit time and the fifth one is assigned a two-hour time of transit. Similarly if six vehicles are assigned to this route, the average time of transit will be $(4 + \Delta 2)/(4 + \Delta) = \frac{8}{6}$, or $1\frac{1}{3}$ hours per vehicle, and so on, so that even though the model discriminates between the first four vehicles and the still further increments that might be made, the result is, nevertheless, to be interpreted as a secured average transit time when a figure of merit is computed.

We now wish to illustrate what we have called "the algorithmic completion of a model." By this we refer to any utilization of mathematical properties possessed by an algorithm in order to obtain access to models which could not otherwise be employed, e.g., because they would otherwise fail to supply valid solutions.

To facilitate construction of a model (i.e., a "literal model") for Fig. 1, we have recourse to the corresponding incidence matrix which is synthesized in Table 1 as follows: The node numbers of Fig. 1 are entered in the stub, and the corresponding links (or connecting

---

*These may be obtained by suitable averaging devices or, if this is not satisfactory and if the relevant probability distributions are available, recourse may be had to the extensions available from chance constraints or stochastic linear programming.[2, 6]

†Other fictions may also be used, of course, but this one was adopted by reference to the kinds of transit time response patterns that were developed by the traffic engineers in this case.

TABLE 1   INCIDENCE MATRIX FOR FIG. 1

Links / Nodes	q_1	q_2	q_3	q_4	q_5	q_6	q_7	q_8	q_9	q_{10}	q_{11}	q_{12}	q_{13}	Stipulations
	1–2	1–6	2–3	2–5	2–5	3–4	5–4	4–9	6–5	5–8	6–7	8–7	8–9	
1	1	1												10
2	−1		1	1	1									0
3			−1			1								0
4						−1	−1	1						0
5				−1	−1		1		−1	1				−2
6		−1							1		1			0
7											−1	−1		−5
8										−1		1	1	0
9								−1					−1	−3
Transit times	5	2	3	1	2	9	3	8	6	2	7	3	4	

branches) are entered in the headings. Then "incidence numbers" relative to the i and j designations on each branch are developed in accordance with the convention *

$$
a_{ik} = \begin{cases} 1 & \text{if link } k \text{ is positively incident on node } \textcircled{i} \\ -1 & \text{if link } k \text{ is negatively incident on node } \textcircled{i} \\ 0 & \text{if link } k \text{ is not incident on node } \textcircled{i} \end{cases} \qquad (18)
$$

The k's are here indexed in association with the variables q, which appear in Table 1 directly above the i–j values that designate the nodes on which the link is actually incident in Fig. 1. Here the convention is to consider positive incidences to appear when the tail of an arrow is incident on a node. Thus in the link 1–2, which is associated with q_1, for instance, these conventions would assign a value $a_{11} = 1$ opposite node $\textcircled{1}$ and $a_{21} = -1$ opposite node $\textcircled{2}$ in the column under q_1. Every other entry in this column would be zero—as is represented by blanks in Table 1—because these are the only two nodes on which this link is incident.

We can now readily form the following model from this matrix, wherein the influxes and effluxes at nodes $\textcircled{1}$, $\textcircled{5}$, $\textcircled{7}$, and $\textcircled{9}$ are asso-

* Other conventions are also possible, of course. See, e.g., Chapter XVII in Ref. 3.

ciated with positive and negative signs, to correspond to these incidence conventions, and the other nodes are accorded zero stipulation values.*

$$\min g \equiv 5q_1 + 2q_2 + 3q_3 + q_4 + 2q_5 + 9q_6 + 3q_7 + 8q_8$$
$$+ 6q_9 + 2q_{10} + 7q_{11} + 3q_{12} + 4q_{13}$$

subject to

$$
\begin{aligned}
10 &= \quad q_1 + q_2 \\
0 &= -q_1 \qquad\quad + q_3 + q_4 + q_5 \\
0 &= \qquad\qquad\quad - q_3 \qquad\quad + q_6 \\
0 &= \qquad\qquad\qquad\qquad\quad - q_6 - q_7 + q_8 \qquad\qquad\qquad (19) \\
-2 &= \qquad\qquad - q_4 - q_5 \quad + q_7 \qquad - q_9 + q_{10} \\
0 &= \quad - q_2 \qquad\qquad\qquad\qquad\qquad + q_9 \quad + q_{11} \\
-5 &= \qquad\qquad\qquad\qquad\qquad\qquad\qquad\quad - q_{11} - q_{12} \\
0 &= \qquad\qquad\qquad\qquad\qquad\qquad\quad - q_{10} \qquad + q_{12} + q_{13} \\
-3 &= \qquad\qquad\qquad\qquad\qquad - q_8 \qquad\qquad\qquad\quad - q_{13}
\end{aligned}
$$

When synthesizing a model, it is often desirable to consider the algorithms and related computer codes available for its implementation. Thus, for instance, an identification of eq. 19 as a linear programming problem might immediately suggest recourse to the simplex method after, first, adjoining

$$q_4 \leq 4 \qquad\qquad\qquad (20)$$

either explicitly or implicitly † to allow for the nonlinearity associated with the flows over the corresponding link.

Further treatments of the model would be required, however, or else the simplex method would have to be altered before this route could be used. The reason is that the simplex method utilizes only nonnegative values of the variables, so that, when applied without modification to eq. 19, this algorithm would produce $q^* \geq 0$, which would be associated with flows only in directions conforming to the arrows shown in Fig. 1. The directions for these arrows were arbitrarily designated, however, and the q_j variables of eq. 19 were not

---

* When associated with the extremal principles we are utilizing, these zero stipulations represent the conservation of current at nodes (Kirchhoff's node law). See Ref. 3, pp. 636 ff.

† See, e.g., the discussion of "bounded variable routines" for modifying the simplex algorithm, as given in Chapter XV of Ref. 3, when it is desired to avoid introducing constraints like those of eq. 20 explicitly.

confined by nonnegativity, so that the counterflows associated with a $q_j < 0$ must be admitted if this will serve to improve the figure of merit g.

It is true that easily made alterations in the simplex algorithm will produce what is wanted here. Nevertheless, we shall assume that such alterations are not to be made * (or are not available) in order to distinguish between a "literal model" and its "algorithmic completion." By a literal model we refer, of course, to a representation such as eq. 19. By its algorithmic completion we refer to a specified solution procedure and its associated mathematical properties. More precisely, we mean that an algorithmic completion has been achieved whenever a literal model and its associated algorithm will, together, produce the solutions that are actually wanted.

In order to modify our literal model of eq. 19 for the indicated application, it is convenient to identify it first with the more general class of models

$$\min \sum_j R_j(q_j)$$

$$\sum_j a_{ij}q_j = E_i \tag{21}$$

Then for any model such as that of eq. 21, which has variables not necessarily nonnegative, we can next observe that the variables which are unconstrained in their sign can be expressed as a difference of nonnegative variables. That is, any q_j which is not constrained in its sign may be associated with two new variables, q_j^+, q_j^-, by means of the relations

$$q_j = q_j^+ - q_j^- \qquad q_j^+, q_j^- \geq 0 \tag{22}$$

so that each q_j, which may be positive or negative, is expressed as a difference of two nonnegative variables. Furthermore, if the simplex algorithm is used, there is no ambiguity since the vectors associated with q_j^+ and q_j^- are linearly dependent and the simplex method utilizes only linearly independent sets of vectors. Hence, when the simplex method is specified, we will have always $q_j^+q_j^- = 0$, which means that at least one of these variables will be zero.

Via a transition of the kind that has been suggested, we can preserve access to the ordinary simplex method, but only in association with a literal model which, in principle, doubles the number of variables in

* Little is lost here by proceeding in the indicated fashion since the literal model we shall utilize also conforms to the way in which the simplex method would be altered.

eq. 19. Also, when nonlinearities such as those represented on the link 2–5 are encountered, it becomes necessary further to increase the number of variables and the number of constraints as well. That is, we would then be considering systems of the form *

$$\min \sum_{j,k} (\rho_{jk}^+ q_{jk}^+ + \rho_{jk}^- q_{jk}^-)$$

subject to

$$\sum_j a_{ij}[\sum_k (q_{jk}^+ - q_{jk}^-)] = E_i \tag{23}$$

$$0 \leq q_{jk}^+ \leq \Delta_k^+ \qquad 0 \leq q_{jk}^- \leq \Delta_k^-$$

wherein

$$q_j^+ = \sum_k q_{jk}^+ \tag{24}$$

represents positive flows on branch j as the sum of the q_{jk}^+, piecewise linear segmental flows, each limited by a stipulation Δ_k^+, and

$$q_j^- = \sum_k q_{jk}^- \tag{25}$$

represents the sum of the negative segmental flows that are limited by their respective Δ_k^- stipulations.† Finally, the coefficients ρ_{jk}^+, ρ_{jk}^- that appear as criterion elements in eq. 23 may be assigned different values, if desired, when treating the different flow directions that are now admitted on the various branches.‡

As has just been seen, a literal model in the form of eq. 23 can be developed for completion by the simplex algorithm. An opposite route might also be employed, of course, possibly to secure an algorithm which might be employed to complete the literal model exhibited in eq. 19 or in even still simpler literal models. For an actual application, however, pursuit of the latter course would generally be pre-

---

* For present purposes we are assuming that techniques such as bounded variable routines, etc. (see preceding footnote), also represent extensions of ordinary simplex methods.

† See eq. 20 for a simple illustration which would here be represented by

$$q_4 = \bar{q}_4 + q_5 = q_{41}^+ - q_{41}^- + q_{42}^+ - q_{42}^-$$
$$0 \leq q_{41}^+ \leq \Delta_1^+ = 4$$
$$0 \leq q_{41}^- \leq \Delta_1^- = 4$$

For this simple nonlinearity only one parallel branch is being utilized but, of course, more would be needed to deal with the more general class of cases represented in eq. 23.

‡ Other more general kinds of anisotropic flow can also be treated. See, e.g., Chapters XVII and XX in Ref. 3.

ceded or accompanied by some consideration for the work which may be needed to synthesize, or discover, such an algorithm as well as the kinds of additional information-generating properties it might possess (e.g., with respect to dual variable solutions). This means, in turn, that one would be considering possible "terms of exchange" between a literal model and its alteration *vis-à-vis* the kinds of algorithmic properties desired and, of course, a most favorable situation obtains when alternative algorithms are already available which possess the kinds of properties wanted.*

The research of recent years has supplied a number of special algorithms—in linear programming and elsewhere—and, in fact, an algorithm is available for the completion of literal models such as in eq. 19.† In this case, moreover, the indicated algorithm has all of the relevant properties, including preservation of the approximating fiction and generation of the dual variables. Thus, we need not repeat our previous discussions of alterations in figures of merit, etc., except to observe that these kinds of problems can also occur when algorithmic completion procedures are used.

MULTICOPY NETWORKS

In Fig. 1 we examined a very simple case in which traffic was originated at only one node. More generally, we would expect traffic to originate at more than one node and, moreover, these separate parts of a total traffic flow would not be under the direction of a single despatcher operating with respect to a known objective.

Under the latter circumstances, a more general problem is confronted as when, say, simulations are to be secured for the traffic patterns that are flowing on a city street network. One approach to this kind of problem may be formulated around a steady-state (equilibrium) principle which was first stated by J. G. Wardrop.[15]‡ This principle can also be restated in a precise form which admits of analytical employment of certain extremal characterizations,§ and one such

* It is possible also, of course, to consider multiple algorithms for use in different parts of an analysis just as it is possible to consider different literal models for use with a single algorithm.

† See Chapter XVII in Ref. 3.

‡ This principle was also utilized by W. Prager, but in a different way than in the approaches we shall examine. See pp. 785 ff. in Ref. 3 for further discussion.

§ The close mathematical relations between "equilibrium" and the ideas of "optimization" can sometimes be used to advantage as part of a general model construction strategy.

approach is by way of polyextremal characterizations, so called because they are directed, really, toward a battery of interacting minimizations which allow for the fact that the transit times on only link
may alter in response to the amount (and direction) of traffic which
is sent over it. In particular, these minimizations are used to produce
traffic pattern simulations in which, at equilibrium, all alternate routes
which are actually used by vehicles traveling between two points will
(a) require the same journey time by an individual vehicle and (b)
will require less time than any alternate unused route.

We may interpret this result by an analogy with the ideas of "substitution" in economic analysis whereby the changing traffic transit
times represent phenomena like the price responses assumed to occur
for supply and demand alterations in general equilibrium models of
market behavior.* Then the situation here becomes analogous to the
one discussed in connection with the measures for functional efficiency
in the section entitled "Some Vector Measures of System Efficiency."
On the other hand, unlike in the case of functional efficiency, the travel
times of all vehicles are also a meaningful magnitude and, when used
with care, they may even be employed as a guide to some of the
choices that might be made when redesigns of the network are being
considered.

To implement such a polyextremal characterization, e.g., for simulation purposes, recourse may be had to theory of n-person games. In
this interpretation, a player is associated with each originating node.
Each such player is then viewed as striving to fulfill his origin-destination requirements at a minimum total time while operating in a network
with resistance characteristics (e.g., the transit times on each branch)
which are partly determined by the actions of other players. Thus,
the resistance characteristics are completely specified for any player
only when the other players' actions are specified.

In this traffic simulation model, there is, in general, no way for the
different players to form cooperating coalitions. Hence, it is reasonable to suppose that the idea of a "Nash equilibrium" may be adopted
from the theory of n-person noncooperative games. This idea is, of
course, based on the assumption that the players will not reform
themselves as cooperating coalitions. On this assumption an equilibrium is achieved in accordance with the following optimality criterion:
No player can deviate from an equilibrium—after it is once attained—

---

* Indeed, for some purposes in economics, the optimizations incorporated in
assumptions like profit maximization, etc., are really only artifacts used to study
the kinds of substitutions that are likely to occur around the resulting equilibrium
states.

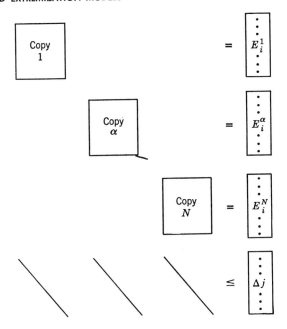

FIG. 2. Schema for a multicopy network.

in such a way that he will improve his total travel time. (Stated differently, such a departure will also correspond to a deviation from Wardrop's principle.)

By this approach, a single network is utilized in association with a multiple minimization, i.e., a polyextremal characterization. Another approach utilizes multiple networks but only a single extremization.

This latter approach will now be illustrated by means of a so-called multicopy network model. For this purpose, we turn first to Fig. 2 and suppose that each of the rectangles contains an algebraic formulation for one copy of the network, e.g., the network shown in Fig. 1, and facsimiles of this copy * are repeated in the other rectangles shown there. Each such network copy has its origin-destination requirements as stipulated in the vertical array of rectangles on the right and, finally, the echelons shown below each rectangle on the left are associated with the nonlinear (but piecewise linear) responses to traffic transit times as different flows are scheduled over this multicopy system.

* Generalizations may be effected to multipage networks, too, in which different rectangles are associated with different networks; see Ref. 7.

To render this more precise, we now provide some analytical representations as follows. For the αth copy we write

$$\sum_j a_{ij} x_j^\alpha = E_i^\alpha \tag{26}$$

where the a_{ij} are incidence numbers and the E_i^α are the effluxes or influxes for the αth copy.

Since the flows may be in either direction—relative to the arrow orientations assigned to each of the network branches—we do not restrict the x_j^α to nonnegative values and, in fact, the resulting signs are used to determine the direction of flow on the jth branch for this segment of the total traffic.

The integrated resistance function of the network will be written

$$R_j(\sum_\alpha |x_j^\alpha|) \tag{27}$$

which is convex and continuous. Thus, combining the preceding two expressions, we have as our model

$$\min \sum_j R_j(\sum_\alpha |x_j^\alpha|)$$

subject to

$$\sum_j a_{ij} x_j^\alpha = E_i^\alpha \qquad \alpha = 1, \cdots, N \tag{28}$$

This model assumes that the R_j values are fixed constants. But, as before, we can extend this to piecewise linearity and utilize a variety of fictions when reproducing the network resistance laws. This can be formalized as in the following model

$$\min \sum_\alpha \sum_j R_j x_j^\alpha$$

subject to

$$\sum_j a_{ij} x_j^\alpha = E_i^\alpha \tag{29}$$

$$\sum_\alpha x_j^\alpha \le \Delta_j$$

where the last set of constraints are associated with the segments assigned to the jth branch that appears in each of the $\alpha = 1, \cdots, N$ copies of the network. These latter constraints are, of course, associated with the diagonals that appear below each of the copy rectangles of Fig. 2, as witness the Δ_j stipulations on their right.

We shall now suppose that algorithmic completion is to be achieved by the simplex method. For this we would then replace the above literal model by one which appears as follows:

$$\min g \equiv \sum_j R_j(x_{j+}{}^\alpha + x_{j-}{}^\alpha)$$

subject to
$$\sum_j a_{ij}(x_{j+}{}^\alpha - x_{j-}{}^\alpha) = E_i{}^\alpha \qquad (30)$$

$$-\sum_\alpha (x_{j+}{}^\alpha + x_{j-}{}^\alpha) \geq -\Delta_j \qquad x_{j+}{}^\alpha, x_{j-}{}^\alpha \geq 0, \text{ all } \alpha, j$$

We have reoriented the last set of constraints so that we can readily obtain access to the corresponding dual maximization problem, which is

$$\max z = \sum_\alpha \sum_i \phi_i{}^\alpha E_i{}^\alpha - \sum_j \psi_j \Delta_j$$

subject to
$$\sum_\alpha \phi_i{}^\alpha a_{ij}{}^\alpha - \psi_j \leq R_j \qquad \psi_j \geq 0 \qquad (31)$$

We now note that the variables $\phi_i{}^\alpha$ and ψ_j are "evaluators" and hence can be used as a set (or vector) of measures for guiding design changes in the system. For instance, consider any optimal $\psi_j{}^*$ value. If it is positive, then anything that can be done to *increase* the corresponding Δ_j value will *decrease* the optimal value of z and, hence, of g as well. Such a Δ_j variation might be accomplished, for instance, by widening the street associated with the jth branch, and this can be evaluated, relative to other possible alterations, by reference not only to the traffic on this branch but also relative to the z which then becomes a scalar measure of total system performance.

We should note, perhaps, that such an alteration may, in general, be accomplished without worsening the position for any vehicle in the system,* although, to be sure, many of the vehicles will not have their travel times improved at all by such an alteration. The case for the evaluators $\phi_i{}^{*\alpha}$ is more ticklish, however. These apply to the influxes and effluxes associated with node i in the αth copy, as represented by the corresponding $E_i{}^\alpha$ stipulations. Formally, we can effect a reduction in travel times—as represented by the new z^* and g^* values—by *increasing* the $E_i{}^\alpha$ values associated with $\phi_i{}^{*\alpha}$ that are negative and *decreasing* the $E_i{}^{*\alpha}$ values associated with positive $\phi_i{}^{*\alpha}$.† Practically speaking, this

---

* Or, if necessary, constraints can be introduced to insure this, e.g., in the initial model. We are here leaving aside conditions which are external to traffic flow considerations only. Such an "external effect" might be experienced if, for instance, the resulting traffic flow alterations cause neighborhood nuisances, alterations in business conditions at different locations, etc.

† That is, the dual variables which are associated with the *equation* constraints of eq. 29 do *not* have their values restricted to nonnegative ranges. See, e.g., pp. 191 ff. in Ref. 3.

would require recourse to devices like rezoning, condemnation, etc., and it can hardly be said that this can be done with respect to traffic considerations only.

Of course, devices like condemnation, etc., are often associated with various schemes for compensating the affected individuals. When this is the case, then these $E_i{}^\alpha$ variations might be studied simultaneously with the Δ_j variations, say, along the lines that were suggested in the first two sections. Those cases, it will be remembered, were directed to securing maximum improvements in a single (optimum) figure of merit.* Of course, such a scalar evaluation measure will not, in general, be satisfactory except on very strong assumptions concerning the fairness and further effects of a compensation scheme. Indeed, even when vector measures are used, such as those discussed in section 3, these problems cannot always be wholly resolved. The difficulties here are well known and have been extensively treated in the economic literature of welfare economics,† and so we need not here go into further detail except, perhaps, to emphasize once more that a scalar measure alone will not, in general, be adequate in any case where multiple goals are involved.

CONCLUDING COMMENTS

The above developments indicated some of the ways in which constrained extremization models may be extended to obtain certain measures for system evaluation purposes. It may be well, therefore, to conclude with some general qualifications and precautions. For this we first introduce some of the general dimensions which Charles W. Morris[11] has suggested for "semiotic" as a general "science of signs." Thus we introduce the following terms:

1. Semantical—the relations between signs and the objects to which they are applicable.
2. Pragmatical—the relations of signs to their interpreters.
3. Syntactical—the relations of signs to other signs.

These three different qualities are ones which Morris suggests for profitable study in connection with any set of signs; hence, with suitable

---

* On the level of national policy such a scalar would be represented by a figure like the gross national product or some similar magnitude whose "growth" is to be improved.

† See, e.g., Refs. 1, 12, or 13 as well as Chapter IX and Appendix D in Ref. 3. A recent discussion of some aspects of these problems in the context of urban planning and redevelopment may be found in Ref. 8.

qualifications, we may point up, succinctly, our final discussion by reference to these categories.

Of course, when artifacts like repricing or reprocessing are employed, the semantical dimensions of the resulting model may have to be approached indirectly. *A fortiori* the pragmatical dimensions may also require careful attention as when, say, the dual of a repriced model is used not only for the purpose of guiding a decentralized operation but also for the purpose of making design changes in addition to those that were already accommodated via the repricing or reprocessing theorems.

The syntactical dimension may be approached most easily in the context of an application wherein the model is to be implemented by means of electronic computations. From this standpoint, then, we may note that the computations will generally be guided by a program for some relevant machine, and the model itself becomes a "metaprogram" in that it establishes general rules for the coding routines that may be considered by the programmer. Notice, however, that the representations provided in a "literal model" only may not be adequate for the syntactical guidance that is needed. For instance, a particular literal model may be identified as a linear programming problem and, hence, be regarded as a candidate for solution by the routines of the ordinary simplex algorithm, whereas a correct solution will be obtained only if the regular simplex routines are modified * or if some other algorithm is specified for "completing the model." Conversely, mere identification of a problem as being nonlinear does not rule out the possible use of a linear model. After all, a distinction can be made between a problem and the way it is modeled, especially where an optimization may be used, possibly as an artifact, to secure the solutions that are wanted.† Within these limits, however, and subject to the qualifications we have indicated in connection with the above artifacts, the maker of a mathematical model is necessarily involved in synthesizing a metaprogram whose syntactical properties may be used not only to guide himself (or others) to an optimum result but also to generate further measures and evaluations that may, in turn, suggest alterations in the model and the systems to which it is being applied.‡   Models

* Of course, some attention needs to be given to the kinds of mathematics which may be used for the modelling. As is well known, for instance, every linear programming problem, which is algebraically stated, has a nonlinear calculus correspond. See, e.g., Chapter XVIII in Ref. 3 and the references cited therein.

† For example, in order to secure access to the nonlinear powers of the simplex method; see, e.g., Chapter X in Ref. 3.

‡ For discussions of model making as a new branch of metamathematics, see 14 and the references cited therein.

have often been used to point toward improvement and even discovery of new models. Where evaluation measures for design purposes are concerned, however, this kind of evolution must be handled in an orderly and careful manner, especially where complex system considerations are involved.

REFERENCES

1. Baumol, W., *Welfare Economics and the Theory of the State,* Longmans-Green, London, 1952.
2. Charnes, A., and Cooper, W. W., "Deterministic Equivalents for Optimizing and Satisficing under Chance Constraints," *Operations Research,* **11,** No. 1, (Jan.–Feb. 1963), pp. 18–39.
3. ———, *Management Models and Industrial Applications of Linear Programming,* John Wiley & Sons, New York, 1961.
4. ———, "Systems Evaluation and Repricing Theorems," *Management Science,* **9,** No. 1 (Oct. 1962), pp. 33–49.
5. ———, and Henderson, A., *An Introduction to Linear Programming,* John Wiley & Sons, New York, 1953.
6. ———, and Thompson, G. L., "Critical Path Analysis via Chance Constrained and Stochastic Programming," *Operations Research* (forthcoming).
7. Charnes, A., and Lemke, C. E., "Multi-Copy Generalized Networks" (Abstract), *Notices of the American Mathematics Society* **5,** p. 525.
8. Davis, O., and Whinston, A., "Economics and Urban Renewal," *Law and Contemporary Problems,* Winter Issue (1961).
9. Koopmans, T. C. (ed.), *Activity Analysis of Production and Allocation,* Cowles Commission Monograph No. 13, John Wiley & Sons, New York, 1951.
    9a. Gale, D., Kuhn, H. W., and Tucker, A. W., "Linear Programming and the Theory of Games."
    9b. Koopmans, T. C., "Analysis of Production as an Efficient Combination of Activities."
10. ———, *Three Essays on the State of Economic Science,* McGraw-Hill Book Co., New York, 1957.
11. Morris, Charles W., "Foundations of the Theory of Signs," *International Encyclopedia of Unified Science* **I,** Part 1, The University of Chicago Press, Chicago, 1955, pp. 79–137.
12. Reder, M. W., *Studies in the Theory of Welfare Economics,* Columbia University Press, New York, 1947.
13. Samuelson, P. A., *Foundations of Economic Analysis,* Harvard University Press, Cambridge, 1947.
14. Tarski, A., "Contributions to the Theory of Models I, II, III," *Indagationes Mathematica XVI,* Proceedings of the Section of Sciences, LXII, Series A, pp. 573–588 and XVII, Fasciculus I, Proceedings of the Section of the Sciences, Series A, No. 1, pp. 56–64.
15. Wardrop, J. G., "Some Theoretical Aspects of Road Traffic Research," *Proc. Inst. of Civil Eng.* (London), Part II (June 1952), pp. 325–378.

CHAPTER 6

THE COMPLEAT CONVERSATIONALIST: A "SYSTEMS APPROACH" TO THE PHILOSOPHY OF LANGUAGE

HILARY PUTNAM

INTRODUCTION

This discussion concerns the basic characteristics of what is coming to be called "systems theory." It is not to be expected that everybody will agree on the scope of that rubric—perhaps, not even that there *is* such a thing as "systems theory"!

Today the woods are full of new sciences and theories, and very often the leading practitioners of a new science or theory are the ones with the gravest doubts concerning the very existence of the alleged science or theory. Whether or not there is such a thing as systems theory, there is something that has come to be called a "systems approach" in diverse fields of science and engineering. Broadly speaking, that approach has two obvious characteristics. First, it is a *model-building* approach—we test our understanding of a process by trying to "simulate" it. Second, the models involved are frequently *not* the continuous models familiar from classical mathematics, physics, and engineering, but essentially discrete structures. Thus the mathematics employed tends to be information theory, recursive function theory, automata theory, etc., in short, "finite mathematics." Not surprisingly, the field of application of this kind of approach turns out to be very wide, and questions concerning military strategy, economic and industrial organization, "mechanical mathematics," linguistics, information retrieval, and control systems have all been approached in this way with some degree of success.

In this chapter I wish to make a premature attempt to treat general questions in the philosophy of language—questions of meaning and function of language—in this way. I say a *premature* attempt, because it is quite obvious that we cannot today "simulate" language use with any degree of success. The Compleat Mechanical Conversationalist—the computing machine with which one can conduct an intelligent and unrehearsed conversation—lies in the distant future. What we *can* do today is *begin* to formulate the general principles upon which the complete conversationalist will operate. In so doing, we may perceive with greater sharpness and clarity than usual the nature of the difficulties involved and the particular defects of the more classical approaches to the philosophy of language. If we can accomplish this, then we may also see why and how the attempt to "simulate" a phenomenon increases our understanding of that phenomenon. Let us begin with some approaches that *will not* work.

STIMULUS-RESPONSE APPROACHES

The first of these approaches is the obvious "stimulus-response" approach. Of course, with *some* definition of "response" and *some* definition of "stimulus," speaking may be a matter of making conditioned (in *some* sense of "conditioned") responses to stimuli.[1] But it is important to recognize just how abstract both stimulus and response are in the language-using situation.

Suppose a parrot could be conditioned to say "biscuit" when and only when a biscuit was presented. Would the parrot "understand" the word biscuit? We shall settle *this* question by fiat: We shall say that the sort of understanding that interests us is the ability to use (and respond appropriately to the use of) words in whole sentences. Clearly, one may be able to use "biscuit" in isolation without being able to use such sentences as, "If she had given me a biscuit, I wouldn't be so hungry." We use and understand every day sentences we have never encountered before. A linguistic theory stands or falls by its ability to shed light on just this phenomenon.

We see right off that many classical "explanations" of this ability are really quite empty, and will not help us at all in our effort to build the Compleat Conversationalist. Suppose we condition a parrot to respond to the presentation of a biscuit with the word "biscuit." How shall we condition it to respond to the absence of a biscuit? Even if we could train the parrot to respond to the question, "Is there a biscuit?" with "no" whenever no biscuit is present, and with the same answer to, "Is there a glass?" when no glass is present, how likely is it that the parrot could generalize in order to obtain the "meaning" of "no"? Suppose we train the parrot to respond with "orange" whenever an orange is present. Will it then "project" the answer "no" to the question, "Is there an orange?" (when no orange is present)? A child will but a parrot will not; that is the essential difference between the child and the parrot.

Let us analyze this "projection" a little. What is required is, so to speak, a metaconditioning. The parrot (or the child) must learn that whereas "biscuit" is an appropriate response to a biscuit (at least in baby talk), and "glass" to a glass, "no" is not an appropriate response to a particular kind of object or quality at all. The "rule," to call it that, for the use of the word "no" (in these simple cases) is: If the response "biscuit," "glass"—or whatever *concrete noun* may be in question—is *not* appropriate (not elicited), then the stimulus, "Is there an N?" (where N is the concrete noun in question) is to elicit the response "no." In short: (1) The habit to be acquired is a recursive mechanism in behavior; any learning theory whose concept of habit does not explicitly recognize the central role played in learning by the acquisition of recursive mechanisms will be hopelessly inapplicable here. (I do not know of a learning theory that does explicitly recognize it.) (2) The habit to be acquired involves responding to one's own responses (including inhibitory responses and failures to respond). (3) The habit to be acquired presupposes other habits, namely, those involved in the acquisition of the *syntax* of one's native language. Studies have shown * that 2½-year-old children already sort out

* These studies (as yet unpublished) have been conducted by Roger Brown at M.I.T. and Harvard.

(and behave differentially toward) nouns, adjectives, articles, and verbs. It is clear [2] that we learn to speak in part by learning to implicitly classify words as nouns, concrete nouns, abstract nouns, etc., to "parse" sentences, unconsciously if not consciously, and to pay attention to syntactic distinctions and patterns. Chomsky has argued convincingly that this "internalizing" of the grammar of one's native language is itself a process which involves a highly structured system of recursive mechanisms, and which is independent of *meaning*. We all recognize that "the dog looks hungry" is well formed and that "the dog looks barking" is not, although both are meaningful, and that "colorless green ideas smoke furiously" is well formed and that "furiously smoke ideas green colorless" is not, although both are meaningless (both examples are Chomsky's). Indeed, the psycholinguistic evidence is that the moron recognizes that "colorless green ideas smoke furiously" is well formed in just the way that the linguist does—by seeing that it has the "structure" $\text{AdjAdjN} + \text{VAdv}$, although the linguist does this consciously and the moron unconsciously.

    I speak of the rule to answer "no" to "is there an N?" where N is a concrete noun, if the situation does not elicit N—as a *recursive* mechanism for two reasons: (1) It can easily be generalized (once the full grammar has been internalized) to a rule for assenting to *negations* of sentences, and the negation transformation [3] is one that "generates" a potential infinity of sentences. (2) Even in its unextended form, the rule applies to an "open class" of utterances since the concrete nouns are an open class. The second reason is not a very good one by itself, since not every rule referring to an open class has the iterative character that leads us to apply the term "recursion." However, if we consider the first reason, and think of this rule as joined to other rules for employing the other logical connectives, the sense in which the whole battery of rules in question is "recursive" will quickly become clear. (Consider, for example, the process of deciding whether to respond "yes" or "no" to "either there is a glass and no biscuit or there is an orange and two apples.")

    Chomsky has argued in his review of Skinner [1] that ordinary stimulus-response theory is empty when it comes to accounting for the acquisition of just the habits of *syntactic* recognition discussed in the foregoing. It is empty precisely because it *fails* to take a "systems approach," i.e., to view the language user as a mechanism containing recursive devices for scanning sentences, assigning words to form classes, parsing sentences, etc. Since Skinner, in particular, does not recognize the presence of these devices, he does not see that *they* are the "habits" to be explained. Instead, he sees the sentence "the second world war wrought great havoc" as an *isolated* response for which he has then to seek a stimulus. Not surprisingly, the result of his search is empty; Skinner takes this sentence to be a response to a stimulus which he identifies with the *second world war* itself! It is clear that, if building the Compleat Conversationalist requires the construction of a computer which has to associate appropriate stimuli with sentences *sentence by sentence,* and if the stimuli are to be objects as intangible as the whole second world war, then we shall never be able to build the Compleat Conversationalist. But let us not despair; if Chomsky is right, Mother Nature has not been able to build the actually existing complete conversationalists on *those* lines either!

THE "PRINCIPLE OF ACQUAINTANCE"

In a series of publications,[4,5] Gustav Bergmann has argued for the "principle of acquaintance," introduced by Bertrand Russell at the beginning of the century, as an adequate account of meaning. Let us test its adequacy by trying to "simulate" it. We shall quickly see that there is a hitherto unnoticed equivocation at the bottom of this principle. In the process we shall see again that, "How would this theory of language, if correct, enable us to *simulate* language-using?," is a question which detects pseudoexplanations and exposes question-begging accounts for just what they are.

The principle of acquaintance asserts that understanding whole sentences is a very simple business. To understand a sentence, one has merely to understand the words that make it up. (Thus the contribution of *word order* is neglected from the outset.) To understand epistemologically "primitive" words, one has merely to learn their meaning by "acquaintance," in the way in which a child might learn the meaning of "biscuit" by hearing biscuits called "biscuits" often enough.

One difficulty is apparent at once—the ability to use the logical operators and connectives, *not, and, or, all, is,* is taken for granted by this theory. We have already seen that even in "baby talk" this is a complicated story. Similar difficulties arise with tense endings, abstract nouns, etc. Thus, consider the sentence, "A boy was here three days ago." I can learn to use "boy" in very trivial situations, parrot-fashion. Perhaps "here" could be similarly acquired, although this is doubtful. "Three" has been taught "ostensively" to white rats, i.e., they have been taught to discriminate piles of three objects, independently of composition. Thus we can imagine a child learning "three" as a response to an observable feature of a presented situation. Perhaps the child could learn to associate "day" with a certain interval of time by being taught to say "day" when another day has elapsed after a certain designated starting event (e.g., someone saying "now"). But what of the "was"? We might use pigeon English and simply say, "Boy here three day ago" (what of "ago"?). Perhaps "ago" could be learned in "while ago" (which might be shortened, baby-talk fashion, to simply "ago," to indicate that something has already happened). Then the child uses "ago" in certain situations. (For example, "Did you drink your milk?" "Ago.") The child uses "boy" when confronted with a boy, at least sometimes. The child uses "here." The child uses (stretching imagination to the utmost) "day" as a response to a whole day as stimulus. (For example, we imagine the father saying, "I'll give you a tricycle in a day," and the child running up precisely one day from the time of utterance and saying "day.") The child uses "three" when confronted by a pile of three objects, independently of composition. So the child must understand the *sentence*, "Boy here three day ago." Obviously not!

So many things have gone wrong that it is difficultt to know where to begin. Consider, for example, the difference between "boy here three day ago" as a sequence of five one-word sentences, as a single sentence, and as a mere list of words!

Coming to the context of "simulation," the same point is even clearer. If I build a machine which can use each word in a sentence (considered as a one word utterance) in response to an appropriate "stimulus," it does not at all follow that it will be able to use that sequence of words *considered as a sentence*. It also does not follow that there will be such a thing as an appropriate stimulus. Many sentences are not under any particular reality controls. "There was a boy here one million days ago" could occur in any extralinguistic context, and in a great many linguistic settings. So could "normal air pressure is fifteen pounds per square inch," to take a less bizarre example.

All this may seem very unfair to Bergmann and Russell. They have, after all, a very easy retort: the child, in my example, or the machine, does not have the *concepts* "day," "here," "ago," "three," "boy" completely but only partially. It has them partially since it can use the words in some contexts. But the fact that it cannot understand them when they are put together in a sentence shows that there is an incomplete grasp of at least one of the concepts. But this retort is *too* easy—it gives the show away. What we see is that the principle as far as we stated it (there is another part relating to defined terms which is not relevant here) rests on an equivocation. Consider the principle again: "To understand the words that make up a sentence is to understand the sentence." This part of the principle is a tautology if "understand" is taken in the way we indicated, namely, as the ability to employ words in the sentences of the language. (I assume that the sentences contain only words we understand, and that there is a reasonable bound on complexity.) If we can use all the words in a sentence in any sentence containing only those words, then we can use that sentence. Consider the other part of the principle: "To understand a word is to associate the word with the appropriate quality." This is *false* if "understand" is taken as we just took it, and doubtfully true if "understand" means to "be able to use the word as a one-word response utterance to that quality as stimulus." Only by equivocating between the two senses of "understand" can *both* halves of the principle ever be made to appear plausible at once.

TWO MODELS FOR THE COMPLEAT CONVERSATIONALIST

It is possible to extract a model for the semantic abilities of a *speaker* from Reichenbach.[8] Like the other model to be presented, it is radically oversimplified. But radical oversimplification requires no apology at this stage of the game.

Reichenbach's model starts in assuming the existence of a class of basic sentences which we shall call *observation sentences*. The use of these is fixed by a rule of the following form: Assert S if and only if S^* is satisfied, where S^* is a condition that the speaker can detect without the use of special instruments. For example, S might be, "There is a crow in front of me," and the rule directs the speaker to assert this if and only if there is a crow in front of him, where we assume that his sense organs are able to ascertain whether or not this is the case. (Later Reichenbach considers the problem that it is sometimes desirable to revise observation sentences in order to preserve theories, but we shall neglect this here.) Secondly, the speaker is assumed to have internalized a system of rules of deductive and inductive logic. He may be thought of, for our purposes, as a computing machine which computes "weights" for sentences, subject to certain restrictions. Let us suppose that the Compleat Conversationalist utters sentences whose weight exceeds a certain critical number. Then, if he has seen many black crows but no white ones, he will say, "All crows are black." And if he later sees a white one, he will say, "No, some crows are not black." So he will use the word "all" correctly.

Notice that this model assumes that the ability to use sentences is not sharply separated from the ability to make inductive inferences.

A more interesting case (discussed by Reichenbach) is one where a speaker sees a great many trees and shadows. He comes to assign a high weight to the assertion that every tree shadow stands in a certain spacial relation to a tree. Now he sees a tree shadow; but he is so situated that he cannot see whether there is a tree in the appropriate place or not. (His system of inductive logic must be so constructed that cases in which he is not in a position to confirm or disconfirm a statement because he cannot see the region referred to in the statement are distinguished from falsifying cases.) So he deduces from the generalization he has "accepted," together with the observation statement that there is a tree shadow, the new statement that there is a tree in a certain place which he is not observing, say, "There is a tree behind me." Thus specific statements about unobserved objects can automatically be asserted by the Compleat Conversationalist once it has been given enough deductive and inductive logic. Of course, this is not meant as an argument to convince the sceptic who doubts even the existence of unobserved places and times. But this was not Reichenbach's purpose. Reichenbach was showing how such inferences can be made within the normal framework of, say, a four-dimensional infinite world. At the same time—and this is what is of importance to us now—he was showing how the positivists' problem of "reducing" such statements to statements about observables simply does not exist; once we have learned to conclude inductively to such statements we have learned to use, or if you like, to "understand" them, and no further reduction is necessary or possible.

The second model that I will present is called "the Carnap model." It has not been presented by Carnap, but its relation to Carnap's work will become clear as I proceed. This is a model for the semantic abilities of the *hearer* rather than the speaker. We begin by assuming a hearer who believes everything that he is told. Also we assume an ideally "rational" hearer in the deductive and inductive logician's sense.

Our language, this time, will be not a natural language, like English or French, but a formalized language of the sort studied by Carnap.[6] The various "possible worlds" (relative to the description afforded by the language) are describable by certain infinite sets of sentences called "state descriptions." In fact, each maximal consistent set of sentences corresponds to a possible world, and exactly one such set must hold in any universe. If we had a developed measure of the "consistency" of a set of sentences in a natural language,[7] this notion of a maximal consistent set or state description could also be extended to natural languages, but the development of such measures is today in its infancy. However, the Compleat Conversationalist is a somewhat unnatural "person," so it is only fitting that he speak an "unnatural language," at least to begin with. If a sentence belongs to a certain maximal consistent set, we say that it "holds" in that possible world or state description. Each sentence holds in a certain class of state descriptions, and this class is called by Carnap the *range* of the sentence. This range can actually be computed by using a certain way of describing the state descriptions, and by relying on the way in which the sentence is built up out of predicates, truth functions, quantifiers, etc. We shall visualize the Compleat Conversationalist as consisting, in part, of a device which is able to make precisely this computation.

Notice that this model fully exploits the grammatical structure of the language in semantical analysis. This may not be obvious from these brief remarks, but an examination of the inductive definition of "range" in any single case will establish the point—the Compleat Conversationalist will have an entire "internalized grammar" of the language. That is, it will have the ability to tell grammatical sentences (sentences for which it can compute a range, using the rules) from ungrammatical sentences. Actually, the dependence of the inductive definition of range on the grammar is far more extensive than this; but this is not the place to go into details.

Secondly, our "hearer" will be characterized by two measure functions over state descriptions: one a utility function which measures his preference for one state description over another, and the second, a "subjective probability metric," which determines his absolute and conditional probability assignments in accordance with the usual theorems of the probability calculus. We will require that the probability metric be "inductive" in Carnap's sense: intuitively, this means that it must permit one to "learn from experience" (carry out inductive inferences, at least of a simple kind).

What happens now is that one says things to this hearer; he believes those things; and this modifies his behavior. How does it modify his behavior? Since this is what Carnap would call a "logical" theory of an ideal hearer, as opposed to a "psychological" theory of an actual hearer, let our hearer obey Carnap's recommendation—he will always act so as to maximize his estimated utility. Then his behavior is completely determined. If we know the choices open to him, we can, in principle, say how he will behave in any situation, and how his behavior would have been different if one had (*a*) said something different to him or (b) if he had construed the words differently (assigned a different range).

This model, it turns out, has both a pessimistic and an optimistic aspect. The cause for pessimism (if things are as "bad" as this model suggests) is that one cannot characterize the meanings of utterances in terms of the behavior of *hearers* at all! For saying anything to a hearer may cause him to do anything, if he has a "bizarre" utility function. Of course, it may be that in certain respects human utility functions do not differ very much, and that for this reason some utterances (e.g., "Fire!") produce fairly predictable behavior in hearers who believe them. However, by and large, I think that pessimism probably *is* warranted as far as the program of characterizing the meanings of utterances in terms of extralinguistic behavior of hearers is concerned.

The optimistic aspect is that the study of the semantical abilities of hearers falls rather naturally into three parts. The third part, the study of utility functions, seems best excluded from *linguistic* theory altogether. (Its presence, however, is the reason that a "model" of a language speaker or hearer is such an impossible thing; language skills are the only skills that cannot be modeled without modeling a whole human being.) The first part, the inductive definition of range, corresponds naturally to grammar and to semantics in the narrow sense (paraphrasing, synonymy relations, etc.). The middle part, inductive logic, is the most intriguing. It may not be too hard to do, at least in a simplified form, and it may shed some light on the abilities of both speaker and hearer.

We have now seen, in a very preliminary way, what the structure of the Compleat Conversationalist might be. If we complicate the model so as to introduce "speech acts" other than *assertion*—say, giving commands or asking questions—then still other dimensions of the "life" of a community of Compleat Conversationalists (for they will have to form a community, if they are to give each other orders, ask questions, etc.) would have to be sketched. All this is in principle possible, however formidable the task may appear today. Let us now contrast this approach to language with other approaches of recent and current vintage.

WITTGENSTEIN'S "LANGUAGE GAMES"

Wittgenstein has pointed out that the structured patterns of linguistic behavior (he calls them "language games") we encounter in connection with one word may be quite heterogenous, and he has derided the notion that there is some unitary thing, the "meaning" running through and accounting for all of the language games that we play with one and the same word. Consider the word "wine" for example. We may use it in one situation, e.g., "Have another glass of wine, do." We may use it in another situation, saying, "This is a good wine, but that is better." Or we may use it in the absence of wine, saying, "I was just thinking how nice it would be to have some wine." Common sense holds that in all of these utterances the *word* "wine" is connected with the *thing*. Wittgenstein daringly refers to this alleged omnipresent connection between the word and the thing as *occult*. Perhaps the word "wine" figures in a potential infinity of little playlets (I have just alluded to three), and the "common meaning" of the word resides in the way in which the playlets overlap, crisscross, depend upon one another, and in nothing else?

In order to bring this issue into sharper focus, let us imagine a culture in which wine is never sold but only bartered. Other things are bought and sold; perhaps there is some ancient religious taboo that prohibits the buying and selling of wine. It is occasionally defied, this taboo, but the people who defy it (say, alcoholics) are much despised. In fact, a way of insulting a man is to suggest that he buys or sells wine. In this culture, then, there is a language game which does not exist in ours—insulting a man by saying in his presence that he buys or sells wine; and in our culture there is a language game which does not exist in the first one—the "normal" buying or selling of wine. Common sense would hold that the *word* "wine" has the same meaning in English no matter which culture one is in (these are both to be English-speaking cultures); it is only the beliefs about buying and selling wine that are different in the two cultures. In Wittgenstein's view, as I interpret him, this "sameness of meaning" is a myth. *Most* language games are the same, and this is the only sense in which the meaning is the same. To suggest that the meaning is the same *even in this language game* would be unintelligible.

But would it? Let us see. If the members of both cultures are Compleat Conversationalists, then it is clear that the only difference between the members of the one culture and the members of the other may lie in the utility functions. Since we have decided (not unnaturally, I think) *not* to count the utility functions as part of meaning, it follows that there is *no* difference in meaning. If asked what the sameness of meaning consists of, we can easily answer that, if the sentence, "This is a glass (or bottle) of wine," did not have the *same* range and the same reality controls (when used as an observation sentence), then it could not be used to express the *dis*agreement in values. If I say, "This is a bottle of wine, will you give me a dollar for it?," in the one culture, I get an entirely different response than I do in the other culture because the values have been varied *while the meaning has been held constant.* It is easy to see what "meaning" is here. It is the union of the recursive rules determining the ranges of sentences, the rules assigning reality controls to observation sentences, and certain further rules (the deductive and inductive logic, at least in part, and, in the case of certain "transcendental" terms, e.g., theological terms, theoretical terms in science, it may be a rule that certain assumptions involving the term cannot be denied as long as the term is to have a constant meaning.[7] Of course, this is not really a definition of "meaning," certainly not of the meaning of a word. But that is not what we need. What we need to see is that the hoary distinction between meaning and use has a solid foundation in the fact that the use of linguistic expressions depends on their meaning in the sense outlined in the construction of the Compleat Conversationalist, but it also depends on something outside of the province of linguistics altogether—the values (or "utility function") of the individual speaker or culture.

Notice that, if a whole language—say, English—is held constant in meaning, in the sense indicated, while the culture is varied, then many, perhaps most, of the little playlets that we call language games may be altered. *The sameness of meaning* that nonetheless exists is at the same level as the *sameness of grammar.* It is a *theoretical structure* in the double sense that its description involves theoretical terms ("range," "reality controls," in the case of meaning, "concrete noun," "relative clause," in the case of grammar, as examples), and (assuming here a psycholinguistic theory) that the recognition by speakers of deviations from grammar *or* meaning almost certainly involves the *implicit* use of these same theoretical notions. Wittgenstein conceived of philosophy of language as an enterprise that uses no theoretical terms and to which scientific investigation is irrelevant. He had the right, as an individual, to refuse to admit the whole scientific dimension of the study of language into his system of analysis. But he should not have concluded that common meanings are "occult" unless he was prepared to regard, say, *being a grammatical sentence* as an "occult" property of utterances.

"CAUSAL" AND "RULE-GOVERNED" THEORIES OF MEANING

A dichotomy which runs through theories of meaning or, rather, through the discussion of those theories is the dichotomy between what may be called *causal* theories and *rule* theories. A typical causal theory (Pierce, Morris, Skinner) identifies the meaning of an utterance with its causes and effects. I have already indicated that such theories are mistaken: almost anything may lead me to utter an utterance, depending on my utility function, and almost anything may result from my hearing an utterance. What these theories represent is the danger involved in starting off at the *wrong level of abstraction*. The concrete event of the utterance of a particular utterance with its full battery of causes and effects is much *too* concrete to be of interest. *Rule* theories, by way of contrast, recognize that language is a social phenomenon, and that it is governed by rules. It is a rule, for example, that, if I command someone to shut the door, then some contextually definite door should be open. This rule does not say what will, in fact, cause me to command someone to shut the door on any specific occasion, or whether or not he will obey. But it is a rule connected with the speech act in question, i.e., it is socially recognized that "something has gone wrong" if a command is issued, or apparently issued, to shut the door when the door in question is already shut, and one misexecuting the speech act in this way is open to certain types of criticism. Another rule is that the commander should have some type of socially recognized authority over the commandee, or at least that the commandee should have some sort of socially recognized obligation relevant to the performance of the act in question *vis-à-vis* the commander, be it only that of simple politeness. Again one may utter the command in question although the condition is not fulfilled. The condition is not a natural law which cannot be violated, nor is it a part of the definition of the speech act in question. Often it would still *count* as a command if I ordered you to run out and buy me a package of cigarettes, although I have no right to do so (although sometimes it might not, some misexecutions are so extreme as to defeat the attempted speech act entirely). Still, "something has gone wrong" if I say, apparently in dead earnest, "I order each and every one of you to give me ten dollars," and certain kinds of criticism would obviously ensue. Certain philosophers of language have recently suggested that the rules governing such a speech act as commanding you to shut the door *give the meaning of the utterance in question*. This theory is a special case of the wider theory-type "rule theory." What is common to all rule theories is that they insist that the meaning of an utterance resides in the *rules* governing its employment, and this is something quite different from the causes and effects of particular utterances in particular situations (or even in general).

Where does our systems approach to this problem fall with respect to the dichotomy between rule theory and causal theory? I suggest that it cuts completely across it. What we stress is something that rule theorists and causal theorists both tend to miss—that the central problem, whether at the level of grammar or at the level of semantics, consists of understanding a certain stock of human abilities. The ability to distinguish well-formed from ill-formed sentences, to assign words to form classes, to parse sentences, at least roughly, in the case of grammar, for example; the ability to paraphrase sentences, to distinguish coherent from incoherent sequences of sentences, to distinguish situationally appropriate from situationally inappropriate sentences in the case of semantics, for example. To understand completely these abilities, we have to make progress toward a satisfactory model, toward a simulation, toward the Compleat Conversationalist. In this sense we have a link with the causal theorist, although we are far from the simple associationism that he seems to favor, with our recursive mechanisms and "transformations," even at the level of grammar. At the same time, even in a mere model sketch of the type presented above, we can distinguish components which correspond to what might in a reasonable sense be called linguistic *rules*, i.e., fundamental *patterns* independent of the individual speaker (e.g., of his utility function, though possibly not of the normal range of variation of utility functions) and components which would correspond to merely "causal" factors, important in a psychological theory of the production of utterances but lying wholly outside the province of linguistic theory. For example, if the condition S^* is a reality control on the use of a sentence S as an observation report, then this can be expressed by saying that it is a *rule* of the language that a speaker who has detected S^* should assent to S.

Two general remarks should perhaps be made. First of all, I do not think something should be called a "condition" associated with a speech act or, more generally, a "rule of language" unless a *linguist* could, in principle, detect (possible by questioning the informant) violations of the condition or rule. This would exclude, for example, taking truth conditions as "conditions" in this sense. For example, I do not think it is very helpful or revealing to use the notion "rule of English" in such a way that, "One should not assert that there is life on Mars unless there is, in fact, life on Mars," or, "One should not assert that God exists unless in fact God does exist," come to be classified as rules of English. For a linguist would then have to be an oracle with respect to physical questions, biological questions, theological questions, etc., in order to tell in general whether or not the rules of English were conformed to. Secondly, I think that whether or not an alleged rule of English is *revealing* or not depends upon the extent to which it enables us to understand the whole *system* of linguistic abilities referred to above. For example, those who would include truth conditions as rules of English are obviously guided by two considerations, namely: (1) that such conditions give the meanings of utterances, and this is one of the general goals of rule theorists; and (2) that some kind of criticism is called for if we find that an utterance has been used to make an assertion while the associated truth condition has been violated. The criticism, in fact, is, "That isn't *true.*" The general fact that the truth conditions for an assertion can be given by any good paraphrase follows at once from any adequate theory of *truth,* as Tarski long ago pointed out; so what we are learning is something about *truth,* and not really something important about the meaning of declarative sentences when used to make assertions.

I repeat, then, that this is a case in which the systems approach— i.e., constantly having in mind the idea that linguistic abilities form a structured system which we wish to describe by means of a mathematized model—enables us to distinguish *revealing* formulations of linguistic rules from tautologies and empty jargon. It is my fear that the newly fashionable "speech act" approach *will* turn into an empty jargon unless the standpoint of general linguistic theory, which in this case coincides with the standpoint of this conference, is taken in connection with it.

WORK ACCOMPLISHED

I have discussed some applications of the systems approach which lie outside the province of present scientific work, and which are merely philosophical. I would not like to leave the impression that there is not a body of substantial scientific research in connection with these remarks. Philosophers as such are interested in general questions of meaning and function of language: What is it to *mean* something by a sequence of sounds? *How* do words have meaning? How is language connected with the world and with behavior? These questions may be intended as conceptual questions (how *could* language be connected with the world?; what does "meaning" *mean?*) or as empirical questions. In practice, there is no sharp line between the two, and philosophers of language and working linguists have come to interact vigorously in the last five years. Here I have tried to show how a systems approach may be of help in threading one's way through the maze of the purely conceptual questions; but it has also led to the birth of what some regard as the most exciting development in the whole history of linguistic science, the birth of what Chomsky has called *linguistic theory*. Linguistic theory takes as its task *precisely* the construction of the Compleat Conversationalist, i.e., of a system which will enable us to *understand* and describe in a *revealing* way human linguistic abilities. Applied to grammar, this approach has led to the first adequate statement of just what a grammar is supposed to *do*, and to the development of what are known as *generative grammars*—formal devices which simulate the sentence constructing and analyzing abilities of human speakers. Applied for the first time to semantics by Fodor and Katz,[7] philosophers of language now working at M.I.T., this approach has led to a similar clarification of what I called semantics in the narrow sense—synonymy relations, analyticity, paraphrasing, etc. The power of this approach seems far from exhausted, and perhaps its greatest importance for the philosophy of the social sciences in general lies in that the goal of constructing revealing models may be both more important and more attainable than the traditional goal of stating "laws." Conventional philosophers of science have insisted that a model is of value only insofar as it leads to a set of predictive laws. Grammar is a living counterexample: a formal model of the grammar of a language leads only to the vaguest predictions concerning the actual behavior of speakers, and then only when coupled with the linguist's common sense. This may be unsatisfactory in the long run, but as John Maynard Keynes so aptly put it, "In the long run we'll all be dead." In the past 50 years we have had ample opportunity to see the stultifying effect upon the social sciences of an ideal of scientific theory derived from physics, and the equally stultifying effect of throwing mathematization overboard altogether. The construction of models which are highly structured and revealing of significant aspects of the phenomena studied may be a more manageable goal. The problem of "confirming" such models is not such a serious one as might appear, if we constantly remember the simple fact that the real question in any single case is not whether a given model fits the data perfectly, but whether it does better than its actually proposed rivals.

REFERENCES

1. Chomsky, Noam, Review of Skinner, B. F., "Verbal Behavior," *Language*, **35** (1957) pp. 26–58.

2. ――――, "Explanatory Models in Linguistics," in *Logic, Methodology, and Philosophy of Science* (Suppes, Tarski, Nagel, eds.), Stanford University Press, Stanford, 1962.
3. ――――, *Syntactic Structures*, M. Cravenhage, Amsterdam, 1953.
4. Bergmann, Gustav, *The Metaphysics of Logical Positivism*, McKay Publishing Co., New York, 1953.
5. ――――, *Philosophy of Science*, University of Wisconsin Press, New York, 1957.
6. Carnap, Rudolf, *The Logical Foundations of Probability*, University of Chicago Press, 1950.
7. Katz, Jerrold, "Analyticity and Contradiction in Natural Language," in *Readings in the Philosophy of Language* (Fodor, J. A., and Katz, Jerrold, eds.), Prentice-Hall, Englewood Cliffs, N. J., 1963.
8. Reichenbach, Hans, *Experience and Prediction*, Chicago, 1938.

CHAPTER 7

THE ABSTRACT THEORY OF
SELF-REPRODUCTION

JOHN MYHILL

Insofar as I understand the meaning of the phrase "general systems theory," "systems" is meant to include both biological and man-made systems, and "general" implies a certain amount of abstraction from the details of anatomy and engineering. In this vague sense of the phrase, the discussion of general principles underlying the simulation of lifelike phenomena, in particular reproduction by man-made automata, falls nicely within the discipline of general systems theory. In this chapter I shall consider some principles underlying the simulation of reproduction which are of interest (1) because of their extreme generality and abstractness and (2) because they show that the existence of self-reproducing machines is only a very special case of a much wider phenomenon, the theory of which might conceivably be applied to situations of quite a different kind from those occurring in biological simulation. Roughly we shall show that, granted certain very elementary properties of the "machines" considered, there exist machines whose "offspring" stand in any desired relation to them; for example, the offspring may be a mirror image of the parent, two attached replicas of the parent, a blueprint for building the parent and so on. (Exact) self-reproduction, i.e., production of an offspring *identical* with the parent, is merely the simplest case of this. Finally we shall sketch a proof, from our simple idealized assumptions concerning machines, of the existence of a machine-building machine from which the successive generations of descendants become in a certain sense more and more intelligent.

So much by way of indication of direction and justification of the inclusion of my topic under the heading of general systems theory. Now I shall give some historical background. The origin of the idea of a self-reproducing machine, like most ideas connected with the simulation of life, surely goes back to legendary times. Whether Pygmalion's Galatea is reported to have borne children I do not know, but it seems unlikely that the thought escaped the minds of all Greeks. In the opposite direction (fertilization of a human being by an automaton), I seem to have heard of the son as well as the bride of Dr. Frankenstein's monster. The robots with which this chapter deals, incidentally, avoid commerce of this nature with humans and are chaste even towards one another; nonetheless I would, in all seriousness, be surprised if my methods would not yield some insight into the possibility of sexual reproduction of automata.

The first precise work out of an idea for mechanical self-reproduction, as is well-known, was done by von Neumann. His machine has two forms or, rather, two degrees of idealization. In the less idealized form, the robot floats in a lake in which its "food," i.e., an inexhaustible supply of (presumably electronic) components is suspended: it traps these components and models them into an exact replica of itself. This differs, of course, from what would conventionally be called reproduction in several ways. For one thing, the formation of the offspring takes place outside the parent robot's body, which is probably quite inessential; for another, the food undergoes no chemical changes before or during assembly, which is probably quite essential since such changes would introduce analog elements into what was originally a digital process.

A more abstract form, intermediate between von Neumann's swimming robot and his second, very austere, tessellation model which I will discuss in a moment, was considered by myself in the years from 1958–1959. I used an infinite half-plane, divided into squares like a checkerboard, on which electronic and machine components moved discretely, i.e., between time t and $t + 1$ (seconds after the commencement of the machine's operation) a component C occupying any square could either stay where it was or move one square north, south, east, or west. There are a finite number of types of components, each capable of a finite number of states. Which of the five permissible motions a component undergoes from t to $t + 1$, and which state it goes into, is determined by its own state and that of its four neighbors (north, south, east, and west) at time t [except that for technical reasons instantaneous or rather effectively instantaneous action at a (bounded) distance is permitted in certain situations]. The components of the machine thus act upon each other and upon the environment by changing states and by imparting motions; for vividness, the imparting of motion may be regarded as effected by the pushing or pulling of one component by another which is either temporarily magnetically attached or permanently welded to it. The environment referred to consists of an unbroken stream of components moving at the rate of one square per time unit on a conveyor belt running along the northernmost edge of the checkerboard. On this conception, a self-reproducing machine is a finite array of components on the checkerboard so designed that it will grasp components from the conveyor belt and assemble them so as to form an exact replica of itself.

Von Neumann's second idealization retains the checkerboard image but abstracts from the kinetic aspect completely. Movements of components are idealized into propagations of patterns of states; furthermore, the various types of components are combined into one type of component (disconnected state-graph). Instantaneous action at even a limited distance is avoided, and instead of grasping a needed component from the environment, the machine propagates a state into a previously blank square. Blankness or emptiness, incidentally, is taken as simply another state, and the requirement is made that at any time only a finite number of squares are nonblank. We thus have an infinite plane ruled checkerboard fashion; each square is capable of a finite number of states (the same for different squares); the state of each square at $t + 1$ is determined by the state of it and its neighbors at t. In this mathematically most elegant formulation, self-reproduction means simply that we begin with one replica of a certain pattern on the checkerboard, and after a time we have two.

It is for this (tessellation) model that von Neumann worked out in detail the plan for self-reproduction, i.e., the initial disposition of states and the transition functions. The construction is laborious for quasi-engineering reasons (synchronization, hunting for the child), but its essence is a straightforward diagonal argument. The purpose of this chapter is to isolate and generalize this argument. The following can be visualized for the most part in terms of whatever idealization the reader is most familiar with, or even in terms of something close to actual computers.

To understand what follows, we need at least an intuitive grasp of the notion of a *recursive* (computable) *function*. Roughly speaking, this means a number-theoretic function (mapping of the nonnegative integers into themselves) which can be calculated by a (digital) computer. The argument or arguments are fed in (say, on a tape), and the value is printed out (say, on another tape). Of course, taking this definition literally, even such a simple function as multiplication would not be recursive, because unlimited storage would be required to multiply two arbitrarily large numbers. Recursive function means digitally computable function idealized by the assumption of (potentially) infinite storage. A digital machine with such a storage which operates on one or more tapes each containing a numeral to produce a tape containing a numeral is called a *Turing machine*.

For most of the following, only a few very simple properties of recursive (computable) functions will be needed; they are all obvious on the basis of the foregoing informal description:

Property 1. If $f(x, y)$ is computable, so is $f(x, x)$ as a function of one variable. (The numeral x is simply copied onto two tapes and fed into the two-input machine which computes f.)

Property 2. If $f(x)$ and $g(x)$ are computable, so is $fg(x)$. (Cascading.)

Property 3. The identity function $f(x) = x$ is computable.

Property 4. If $f(x, y)$ is computable, so is $f(x, a)$ for fixed a (as a function of x).

Turing machines will appear in our development as subassemblies of the machines we are really interested in, namely, *machine-building machines*. Such a machine, in a typical case, has one input, into which is fed an instruction which tells it what machine it is to build. The instruction is regarded as a physical object (say, a tape on which a coded circuit diagram is inscribed), not as, e.g., a series of pulses. Since the circuit diagram can be coded by means of a single nonnegative integer, we can regard a machine-building machine as a mapping from nonnegative integers to building operations (seizure and assembly of components in the imagery of the kinematic models). Once a fixed list of components is prepared, their transition functions listed, and a fixed coding of circuit diagrams into numbers is agreed upon, it is not hard to devise a machine with the property that *every* circuit diagram which is fed into it will be at once "obeyed," i.e., it will cause the machine to build the machine having that circuit diagram. Such a machine is called a *universal machine-building machine*, and its existence (or rather something slightly more general) is postulated as an axiom in the formal developments which follow.

Two cautions are in order. If a machine $\mathfrak{M}$ can build any machine whatever, given a suitable instruction, in particular it can build (a replica of) the machine $\mathfrak{M}$ itself. Why then is not $\mathfrak{M}$ equipped with the instruction I to build $\mathfrak{M}$ already a self-reproducing machine? The answer is obvious as soon as the question is stated precisely: The machine $\mathfrak{M}$ with the input I builds the machine $\mathfrak{M}$ with no input at all, and this does not constitute self-reproduction. We wish machine $\mathfrak{M}$ with input I to build machine $\mathfrak{M}$ with input I.

The second caution is more subtle. Edward Moore of Bell Telephone Laboratories has elegantly proved the so-called *Garden-of-Eden theorem*, which states roughly that there are machines which cannot be built. More precisely, and referring specifically to the tessellation model, *there are configurations which can exist only at $t = 0$*. Here by a configuration is meant simply an assignment of states to (a finite number of) squares. If by a machine is meant simply a configuration, it is impossible, in view of this theorem, for there to exist a machine which can build all machines. (Moore's theorem assumes that a certain condition is satisfied by the transition functions, but this condition seems to be satisfied in all interesting cases.)

However, if we revert to my hybrid model, in which there are different kinds of components, the Garden-of-Eden difficulty can be avoided in the following quite natural way. For every kind of component, designate one state as the quiescent state; let the components on the conveyor belt be in the quiescent state at least until they are grasped by the building machine, and let the transition functions have the property that, if any cell C and its four neighbors are each in the quiescent state at time t, then C remains in that state at time $t - 1$. Consider only machines in which all components are quiescent, and assign to each (as part of its description) a method of *starting* it (by activating one or more of its peripheral components—"plugging in"). A machine is thus an ordered pair consisting of a configuration of quiescent components together with a specification of how it is to be started, i.e., what peripheral cells are to be activated and into what states they are to be put. Now we say that the machine $\mathfrak{M}_1$ *builds* the machine $\mathfrak{M}_2$ if, at some time t after $\mathfrak{M}_1$ is started, the quiescent assemblage of $\mathfrak{M}_2$ has been completed, and at the immediately succeeding time $t + 1$ that assemblage likewise has been started. Briefly, "build" is construed to mean "build and start." With these definitions and a reasonably varied collection of hardware, there is no difficulty in constructing a universal machine-building machine. It is not hard to see that by thus redefining the notion of "universal machine-building machine" to avoid Garden-of-Eden trouble, we have not, in fact, restricted the applicability of the self-reproduction theorem derived below to hybrid models: for if, e.g., the (quiescent) machine $\mathfrak{M}$ builds and starts a replica of itself in the sense of the hybrid model, then the machine $\mathfrak{M}'$ builds a replica of itself in the sense of the tessellation model, where $\mathfrak{M}'$ is simply $\mathfrak{M}$ with the appropriate peripheral components activated.

To complete the definition of machine-building machine, let us also allow autonomous machine-builders (i.e., without input-tapes) and also machine-builders with several input-tapes (for the following, two is enough). Let us finally specify that the machines which are to be built (and started) are *whole* machines, i.e., machines with the appropriate number of input tapes attached.

After these preliminaries, we are ready for the formal development. We let $\{\mathfrak{M}_i^{(n)}\}$ ($n = 0, 1, 2$) be an enumeration of n-input machines and $\{I_i\}$ an enumeration of instructions. $\mathfrak{M}_i^{(0)}$ is the machine built by a certain fixed universal machine-builder $\mathfrak{M}_{u_0}^{(1)}$ when the ith instruction is fed in. We write this

$$I_i: \mathfrak{M}_{u_0}^{(1)} \rightarrow \mathfrak{M}_i^{(0)}$$

In general $I_i: \mathfrak{M}_a^{(1)}$ is the 0-input machine which results from affixing the instruction I_i to the 1-input machine $\mathfrak{M}_a^{(1)}$, and $\mathfrak{M}_x^{(0)} \rightarrow \mathfrak{M}_y^{(0)}$ means that the machine $\mathfrak{M}_x^{(0)}$ builds the machine $\mathfrak{M}_y^{(0)}$. Similarly, $[I_i/I_j]: \mathfrak{M}_a^{(2)}$ is the 0-input machine produced by affixing the instructions I_i, I_j to the first and second inputs respectively of the 2-input machine $\mathfrak{M}_a^{(2)}[\emptyset/I_j]: \mathfrak{M}_a^{(2)}$ is the 1-input machine formed by affixing the instruction I_j to the second input of $\mathfrak{M}_a^{(2)}$ and leaving the first input open. Thus by definition

$$I_i: \begin{bmatrix} \emptyset \\ \hline I_j \end{bmatrix} : \mathfrak{M}_a^{(2)} = \begin{bmatrix} I_i \\ \hline I_j \end{bmatrix} : \mathfrak{M}_a^{(2)}$$

Now we are ready to state some axioms from which follows the existence of a self-reproducing machine.

A1. Let f be a computable function; then there is a machine $\mathfrak{M}_a^{(1)}$ such that always

$$I_n: \mathfrak{M}_a^{(1)} \rightarrow \mathfrak{M}_{f(n)}^{(0)}$$

The machine $\mathfrak{M}_a^{(2)}$ consists of two parts: a special-purpose *computer* which prints out the instruction $I_{f(n)}$ when the instruction I_n is fed in, and the universal machine-builder $\mathfrak{M}_{u_0}^{(1)}$ into which $I_{f(n)}$ is fed in order to produce $\mathfrak{M}_{f(n)}^{(0)}$. With f the identity, A1 asserts the existence of the universal machine-builder itself.

B1. There is a recursive function t_1 such that

$$\mathfrak{M}_{t_1(a,b)}^{(0)} = I_a: \mathfrak{M}_b^{(1)}$$

This merely means that we have chosen our enumeration sensibly, i.e., given (a numerical encoding of) the instruction on a tape and (a numerical encoding of) the circuit diagram of a 1-input machine, we can calculate (a numerical encoding of) the circuit diagram of the result of affixing that tape to that machine. It is trivial with any encoding anyone would naturally think of.

From axioms A1 and B1 follows:

T1 (von Neumann). There exists a self-reproducing machine, i.e., a machine $\mathfrak{M}_a{}^{(0)}$ for which

$$\mathfrak{M}_a{}^{(0)} \rightarrow \mathfrak{M}_a{}^{(0)}$$

Proof. Let t_1 be as in axiom B1, and define

$$s(x) = t_1(x, x)$$

then

$$\mathfrak{M}_{s(x)}{}^{(0)} = I_x \colon \mathfrak{M}_x{}^{(1)}$$

and s is recursive (property 1 of computable functions). Consequently, by axiom A1 there is a machine $\mathfrak{M}_b{}^{(1)}$ such that always

$$I_n \colon \mathfrak{M}_b{}^{(1)} \rightarrow \mathfrak{M}_{s(n)}{}^{(0)} = I_n \colon \mathfrak{M}_n{}^{(1)}$$

Now putting $n = b$, we get

$$I_b \colon \mathfrak{M}_b{}^{(1)} \rightarrow I_b \colon \mathfrak{M}_b{}^{(1)}$$

and $I_b \colon \mathfrak{M}_b{}^{(1)}$ is the self-reproducing machine desired.

The generalization referred to at the beginning of this chapter (whereby machines can build mirror images of themselves, print their own circuit diagrams, and the like) is formally:

T2. For any computable function h, there is a machine $\mathfrak{M}_a{}^{(0)}$ for which

$$\mathfrak{M}_a{}^{(0)} \rightarrow \mathfrak{M}_{h(a)}{}^{(0)}$$

Proof. As before, let s be a recursive function such that always

$$\mathfrak{M}_{s(x)}{}^{(0)} = I_x \colon \mathfrak{M}_x{}^{(1)}$$

By property 2 of recursive functions, the function $hs(x)$ is recursive and so by axiom A1 there is a machine $\mathfrak{M}_c{}^{(1)}$ for which always

$$I_n \colon \mathfrak{M}_c{}^{(1)} \rightarrow \mathfrak{M}_{hs(n)}^{(0)}$$

Putting $n = c$, we get

$$\mathfrak{M}_{s(c)}{}^{(0)} = I_c \colon \mathfrak{M}_c{}^{(1)} \rightarrow \mathfrak{M}_{hs(c)}^{(0)}$$

and $\mathfrak{M}_{s(c)}{}^{(0)}$ is the desired machine.

For the construction of a machine of which each generation of descendants outsmarts its predecessors, we need the following generalization of T2.

T3. Let $h(x, y)$ be a recursive function of two arguments. There is then a machine $\mathfrak{M}_d{}^{(1)}$ for which always

$$I_a \colon \mathfrak{M}_d{}^{(1)} \rightarrow \mathfrak{M}_{h(a,\,d)}^{(0)}$$

The proof is analogous to that of T2, except that instead of A1 we use A2. For every recursive function f of two arguments, there is a machine $\mathfrak{M}_a{}^{(2)}$ such that

$$\begin{bmatrix} I_m \\ \overline{} \\ I_n \end{bmatrix} : \mathfrak{M}_a{}^{(2)} \rightarrow \mathfrak{M}_{f(m,\,n)}^{(0)}$$

and instead of B1 we use:

B2. There is a recursive function t_2 such that always

$$\mathfrak{M}_{t_2(a,\,b)}^{(1)} = \begin{bmatrix} \emptyset \\ \overline{} \\ I_a \end{bmatrix} : \mathfrak{M}_b{}^{(1)}$$

These axioms are trivial and are motivated just as A1 and B1.

Proof of T_3. The desired machine is easily seen to be

$$\mathfrak{M}_{t_2(r,\,r)}^{(1)} \qquad (t_2 \text{ as in } A_2)$$

where r is so chosen (it can be by B2) that always

$$\begin{bmatrix} I_a \\ \overline{} \\ I_n \end{bmatrix} : \mathfrak{M}_r{}^{(2)} \rightarrow \mathfrak{M}_{h(a,\,t_2(n,\,n))}^{(0)}$$

For then

$$I_a : \mathfrak{M}_{t_2(r,\,r)}^{(0)} = \begin{bmatrix} I_a \\ \overline{} \\ I_r \end{bmatrix} : \mathfrak{M}_r{}^{(2)} \rightarrow \mathfrak{M}_{h(a,\,t_2(r,\,r))}^{(0)} \qquad \text{q.e.d.}$$

Before constructing a "self-improving" machine, it will be necessary to explain in what sense we mean self-improvement, and for this, in turn, we need to recall a few facts from the theories of formal systems and recursive functions. A *system* in the sense of metamathematics is simply a set of well-formed (i.e., grammatical) sentences formed from the letters of a pregiven (finite) alphabet: the letters are regarded simply as marks and the sentences simply as (certain) strings of these marks. A system is called *formal* if all sentences belonging to it (and no other sentences) can be printed out (successively, separated by blanks) by a Turing machine (without input). Since formulas can be encoded by nonnegative integers, there is no difference, in principle, between recursive functions of expressions (strings of letters of the alphabet) and recursive functions of numbers. Definitions 1 and 2 following do the same for numbers as Definitions I and II respectively do for expressions:

Definition 1. A set M of numbers is called *decidable* or *recursive* if there is a Turing machine which will give output "yes" if an element of M is fed into it, and "no" if any other number is fed in; equivalently if its characteristic function is recursive.

Definition 2. A set M of numbers is called *effectively generable* if there is a Turing machine without input which will print out (successively, separated by blanks) all the elements of M (and no other numbers); equivalently if it (is empty or) has the form $\{f(0), f(1), f(2), \cdots\}$ with a recursive f.

Definition I. A set Ω of strings on an alphabet Δ is called *decidable* (if the usage is appropriate, a *decidable formal system*) if there is a Turing machine which will give output "yes" if an element of Ω is fed into it and "no" if any other string on Δ is fed in.

Definition II. A set Ω of strings on an alphabet Δ is called *recursively enumerable* or (the set of theorems of) a *formal system* if there is a Turing machine without input which will print out (successively, separated by blanks) all the elements of Ω (and no other strings).

For any set Ω of strings (on a fixed alphabet Δ), let $n(\Omega)$ be the set of numbers assigned to elements of Ω or any reasonable coding: then Ω is decidable (recursively enumerable) if and only if $n(\Omega)$ is. In particular, the set of well-formed formulas of a formal system (in the usual sense) is decidable (we can, of course, tell by inspection and without the aid of a computer whether any reasonably short string is grammatically constructed) and the set of theorems of any of the usual semiformalized axiomatic systems is recursively enumerable (which follows from the fact that we know, again in normal cases without the use of a computer, a proof when we see one).

Let now Z be the theory of nonnegative integers under addition and multiplication; its formulas are formed from identities between polynomials by means of the logical operators "and," "or," "if . . . then," "for every number x," "for some number x," and so on. For example, the following formulas say that x is a prime number:

$$\sim(x = 0) \ \& \sim (x = 0^+) \ \& \ (\forall y)(\forall z)(y \times z = x \ \rightarrow \ y = 0^+ \vee z = 0^+)$$

(0^+ means the successor of 0, i.e., 1). Abbreviate the formula above by $P(x)$; then the formula

$$G : (\forall x)(\exists y)(\exists z)(x + y = z \ \& \ P(z) \ \& \ P(z + 0^{++}))$$

asserts the celebrated (unproved) *Goldbach conjecture* to the effect that there are infinitely many pairs of primes differing by 2. Thus we see that, despite the limited vocabulary of Z, one can ask hard questions in z. The vocabulary actually can be regarded as constituted by the following 17 signs:

$$(\ )\ \forall\ \exists\ x\ y\ z\ {}'\ 0\ {}^+\ +\ \times\ \&\ \vee\ \sim\ \leftrightarrow$$

of which $'$ is so used so that

$$x', x'', x''', \cdots$$
$$y', y'', y''', \cdots$$
$$z', z'', z''', \cdots$$

constitute an unlimited stock of variables. To complete the specification of Z, we need to state the *axioms* [e.g., the axiom

$$(\forall x) \sim (x^+ = 0)$$

stating that 0 is not a successor, and the axiom

$$(\forall x)(\forall y)(x^+ = y^+ \to x = y)$$

stating that no two numbers have the same successor] and the *rules* (e.g., *modus ponens*) whereby new theorems are generated for the axioms and from theorems already proved. It is not to our purpose to list the axioms and rules here; they can be found, e.g., in Kleene's *Introduction to Metamathematics*, page 82.

Now for the application to self-improving machines. Z is a *formal system* which means that we can program a Turing machine $\mathfrak{M}_a{}^{(0)}$ to print out all its theorems and nothing else. We have no guarantee that such a machine would be able to "answer all arithmetical questions," i.e., to print out for each formula f of Z either f or its denial. In particular, no one knows how to prove or disprove, e.g., the formula G above by using all the more high-powered resources of analytic number theory *a fortiori* with the relatively meagre resources available in Z. According to Gödel's celebrated incompletability theorem, this is no accident due to the inadvertent omission of some needed axioms from Z. The theorem in question states that *there is no formal system that contains as theorems all of the arithmetical truths and none of the falsehoods.* In fact, if we are given a formal system of arithmetic (i.e., a system S in the symbolism of Z all of which theorems are true), we can *effectively* find a "better" system, i.e., a system S' in the same symbolism, all of which theorems are true and some of which theorems are not among the theorems of S. Translated in machine language, this result reads as follows: There is a computable function g, such that, if $\mathfrak{M}_a{}^{(0)}$ is a Turing machine which prints out only arithmetic truths, then $\mathfrak{M}_{g(a)}{}^{(0)}$ is a Turing machine which prints out all the arithmetic truths that $\mathfrak{M}_a{}^{(0)}$ prints out, and others too. Thus, if $\mathfrak{M}_{a_0}{}^{(0)}$ is a particular arithmetical theorem-proving machine, for example, if it is a machine designed to print out all and only the theorems of Z, then

$$\mathfrak{M}_{a_0}{}^{(0)}, \; \mathfrak{M}_{g(a_0)}^{(0)}, \; \mathfrak{M}_{gg(a_0)}^{(0)}, \; \cdots$$

is an infinite sequence of better and better arithmetical theorem-proving machines. We express this by writing

$$\mathfrak{M}_{a_0}{}^{(0)} < \mathfrak{M}_{g(a_0)}^{(0)}, < \mathfrak{M}_{gg(a_0)}^{(0)} < \cdots$$

where $\mathfrak{M}_a{}^{(0)} < \mathfrak{M}_b{}^{(0)}$ means that (1) $\mathfrak{M}_b{}^{(0)}$ prints out all the strings that $\mathfrak{M}_a{}^{(0)}$ prints out, and others too, and (2) all the strings that $\mathfrak{M}_b{}^{(0)}$ prints out are true statements of arithmetic.

Now I shall describe informally the promised construction of a machine of which the successive generations of descendants become more and more intelligent in the sense of being able to print out more and more arithmetic truths (and no falsehoods). The machine consists of three parts: an *instruction* I_a, a *machine-builder* $\mathfrak{M}_b{}^{(1)}$ into which I_a is inserted, and a *Turing machine* $\mathfrak{M}_c{}^{(0)}$ which is mechanically attached to $I_a \colon \mathfrak{M}_b{}^{(1)}$, with no information flow in either direction. We symbolize this by

$$I_a \colon \mathfrak{M}_b{}^{(1)} + \mathfrak{M}_c{}^{(0)}$$

where denotes the "inert" juxtaposition of two machines.

Let a_0 and g be as above, i.e., let g be recursive and let

$$\mathfrak{M}_{a_0}{}^{(0)}, \mathfrak{M}_{g(a_0)}^{(0)}, \mathfrak{M}_{gg(a_0)}^{(0)}, \cdots$$

be a sequence of "better and better" theorem-proving machines. We let $c = a_0$, and we want to choose x and b so that when the machine $I_a \colon \mathfrak{M}_b{}^{(1)} + \mathfrak{M}_{a_0}{}^{(0)}$ is started, the following will happen. I_a will "order" $\mathfrak{M}_b{}^{(1)}$ to build three things: first $\mathfrak{M}_{g(a_0)}^{(0)}$, then a replica of $\mathfrak{M}_b{}^{(1)}$ itself, then an instruction I_a, which will "order" the new $\mathfrak{M}_b{}^{(1)}$ to build three things: first $\mathfrak{M}_{gg(a_0)}^{(0)}$ then a second replica of $\mathfrak{M}_b{}^{(1)}$, then an instruction $I_{a''}$ which will "order" the third $\mathfrak{M}_b{}^{(1)}$ to build three things, etc.; schematically,

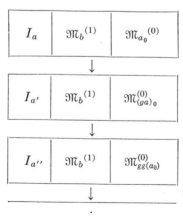

What we seek therefore, is a machine $\mathfrak{M}_b{}^{(1)}$ with the following property. When an instruction I_x is fed into it, it will produce the machine

$$I_{g(x)}: \mathfrak{M}_b{}^{(1)} + \mathfrak{M}_{g(x)}{}^{(0)}$$

For then we have

$$I_{a_0} = \mathfrak{M}_b{}^{(1)} + \mathfrak{M}_{a_0}{}^{(0)} \;\rightarrow\; I_{g(a_0)}: \mathfrak{M}_b{}^{(1)} + \mathfrak{M}_{g(a_0)}$$
$$\rightarrow\; I_{gg(a_0)}: \mathfrak{M}_b{}^{(1)} + \mathfrak{M}_{gg(a_0)}$$
$$\rightarrow\; \cdots$$

The existence of such a machine $\mathfrak{M}_b{}^{(1)}$ follows from T3, if we choose h so that $h(x, y)$ is an index in the enumeration $\{\mathfrak{M}_i{}^{(0)}\}$ of the

$$I_{g(x)} = \mathfrak{M}_y{}^{(1)} + \mathfrak{M}_{g(x)}{}^{(0)}$$

For the full formalization of this construction we need only assume the following additional axioms, of which B3 is trivially motivated, C is dependent on a fairly careful selection of hardware (so that the building and computing parts of a building-and-computing machine will not obstruct each other's activities too seriously: there seems no difficulty in principle), and D is a mere restatement in machine language of Gödel's incompletability result.

B3.   There is a recursive function t_3 such that always

$$\mathfrak{M}_{t_3(x,y)}^{(0)} = \mathfrak{M}_x{}^{(0)} + \mathfrak{M}_y{}^{(0)}$$

C.   If $\mathfrak{M}_x{}^{(0)} \rightarrow \mathfrak{M}_y{}^{(0)}$, then $\mathfrak{M}_x{}^{(0)} + \mathfrak{M}_z{}^{(0)} \rightarrow \mathfrak{M}_y{}^{(0)}$.

D.   There is a machine $\mathfrak{M}_{a_0}{}^{(0)}$ and a recursive function g such that for every sequence of machines $\{\mathfrak{M}_x{}^{(0)}\}$ we have

$$\mathfrak{M}_{0x}{}^{(0)} + \mathfrak{M}_{a_0}{}^{(0)} < \mathfrak{M}_{x_i}{}^{(0)} + \mathfrak{M}_{g(a_0)}^{(0)}$$
$$< \mathfrak{M}_{x_2}{}^{(0)} + \mathfrak{M}_{gg(a_0)}^{(0)}$$
$$< \mathfrak{M}_{x_3}{}^{(0)} + \mathfrak{M}_{ggg(a_0)}^{(0)}$$
$$< \cdots$$

With these assumptions, the existence of a machine of which each generation of descendants outsmarts its predecessor can evidently be stated and proved formally as:

T4.   There exists an infinite sequence of machines $\{\mathfrak{M}_{z_i}{}^{(0)}\}$ such that we have simultaneously

$$\mathfrak{M}_{z_i}{}^{(0)} < \mathfrak{M}_{z_{i+1}}^{(0)}$$

and

$$\mathfrak{M}_{z_i}{}^{(0)} \rightarrow \mathfrak{M}_{z_{i+1}}^{(0)} \qquad i = 0, 1, 2, \cdots$$

We do not seriously envisage (at least not without very substantial further work) the application of C4 to the construction of a self-improving theorem-proving machine. For one thing, the sequence of formal systems $Z, Z', Z'', Z''', \cdots$ is a hopelessly idealized and brutal parody of the growth of intelligence in any usable sense. On the other hand, it seems to me that the possibility of producing an infinite sequence of varieties of descendants from a single program is methodologically significant in a manner which might interest biologists more than artificial intelligences. It suggests the possibility of encoding a potentially infinite number of directions to posterity on a finitely long chromosomal tape, a possibility which seems hitherto to have escaped the notice of biologists.

CHAPTER 8

ENTITATION, ANIMORGS, AND OTHER SYSTEMS

R. W. GERARD

Of systems, the minutest crumb
Must Be, Behave, and then Become.
This Principle the space traverses
From Atoms up to Universes.
And systems that are not malarky
Must find their place in this hierarchy.

                              K. B.

As I am a biologist, I shall discuss in part that particular system—man—that creates general systems theory, operations research, philosophy, science, art, and, in general, the artificial environment in which we live.

Russ Ackoff has said that general systems theory is really a theory of theories; also that, while reductionism does allow one to go from the more complex and general to the simpler, it is not possible to go in the reverse direction. It is certainly true, in the development of the nervous system, that behavior changes from the generalized to the particular, as in reflex responses, and perhaps it is also true that some deductions can come without prior inductions; but I believe that the reverse—moving from the particular to the general—is also possible, and I shall discuss this later.

It seems to me that operations research deals directly with raw systems, before they have been fragmented into the particular parts which are ordinarily dealt with by the existing specialized disciplines, rather than with a theory of systems or a theory of theories. It is integrative but not necessarily highly abstracted.

The present disciplines arose from the study of real systems: geometry from the effort to set land boundaries, astronomy in connection with timing as well as foretelling, botany from the search for drugs, and physiology from the study of malfunction, the latter two being really daughters of medicine used in an effort to handle illness. More-

119

over, at any stage of human development, knowledge from all sources was focused on a given problem—of weather prediction, of foretelling events, of astrology, etc. As a coherent body of dependable fact grew, and with it a sufficiently generalizing understanding to give some reasonably powerful models, particular disciplines of knowledge split off from the unstructured collective pool of human experience.

As some problems were solved, more complex living was possible, or the deeper insights attained raised new questions; so new problems emerged for solution. This always has led to coalescences, with such cross disciplinary disciplines as geochemistry, cytochemistry, astrophysics, biophysics, physiological genetics, neuropsychopharmacology, etc. Now, with the basic problems of human survival solved, the rapid evolution of social man is creating ever new and more complex systems, e.g., the monetary, communication, man-machine, weapon, educational, and like systems. These involve material and human components and their own complex internal structures and interface relationships. Moreover, the old systems have themselves evolved and become more complex, e.g., the nervous system itself.

Accordingly, still new kinds of solutions must be sought by new techniques. Again efforts to coalesce existing separate strands of expertness have led to operations research and behavioral science and systems engineering, all, again as in the more promitive stages, attempting an interdisciplinary attack on complex raw systems. Thus, the operations researcher or the behavioral scientist or systems engineer may mount an integrated systems attack on problems such as mental health, peace, delinquency, traffic, and decision making, attempting, just as did the necromancer of past centuries, to mobilize all available knowledge and wisdom in predicting and ultimately controlling future events. The new disciplines that will fragment out (the new university departments of the future) will thus be more or less orthogonal to the present ones, as the new problems are to the old. Thus, the warp and woof of the renewing cycle of problem, understanding, solution, problem.

Through all this runs the basic question, "What is a system?" This is an element sufficiently whole and independent and internally organized to deserve separate study. The recognition or discovery of such entities must precede their scientific examination. Such qualitative decisions must always precede quantitative ones, if the latter are to be worthwhile; and the important advances in human thought always involve a shift in the entities of concern. This qualitative recognition of the important systems, which I find helpful to call "entitation," is far more important than their measurement. Entitation must precede quantitation; only when the right things have been found to measure are measurements worthwhile.

Many thinkers regard a nonmaterial system, such as language or mathematics, as a complete system in its own right. I find it more congenial to include the dynamics in each case, which clearly involves humans as the makers, users, and modifiers of such disembodied systems. "Real systems," in my thought, necessarily include material entities and exist in real space-time. I proposed the term "org" (reduced from organism) as a general term for these, some years ago, but it has not acquired wide usage. (I am pleased to see it come to life by the initials of the Operation Research Group.) As a subdivision of orgs, it was further helpful to recognize the subclass of animorgs, a type of self-adaptive system that has the properties of complex organization in dynamic equilibrium, regulated behavior, and the ability to change, grow, and reproduce. The concept of animorg has been developed elsewhere,[1] and need not be further presented here. It is, however, pertinent to look at some of the actions of organisms (a subclass of animorgs, which also includes societies or epiorganisms) in relation to the problem of entitation.

Henry James well said, "Life is all inclusion and confusion while art is all selection and discrimination"; and Whitehead similarly pointed out that, "Nature doesn't come as clean as you can think it." Actually, organisms continually do clean up nature and do turn it into art, science, philosophy, or even simple percepts, by very powerful and widespread sensory and neural mechanisms. The sense organs and nervous system of even primitive invertebrates act so as to dissect material objects from their surroundings and thus present clean-cut material entities to the integrating and decision-making parts of the nervous system. Man's grappling with the confused and excessive information input from his sensory universe begins by recognizing material objects, more or less constantly present, and with sizes and durations commensurate with his own. The mechanism of lateral inhibition, now widely identified and well understood in the sense organs and brain, emphasizes boundaries or edges and, since man depends overwhelmingly on vision, thus gives him the material objects for perception and thought. These are the "things" of our existence—the nouns of language. Similarly, on the motor side, one coordinated response is dissected out from a smearing with others by the same mechanism of lateral inhibition; and, no less, does such an ingenious machine in the nervous system cause moods to be clear cut, attention to be directed to one thing or another, ideas to remain coherent, and one plan of action rather than another to be selected. Here then is the mechanism of entitation, or at least a very important part of the mechanism, that gives us single material entities for concern.

After this first stage, both in the development of the individual relating to his world and in the collective growth of racial sophistication and science in relation to the total world picture—the stage of entitation—come many further developments. It is recognized that entities are not uniformly distributed in their attributes, but that certain ones tend to cluster together, and generic terms like cat or dog are added to individual ones like Tabby or Fido. The problem of grouping, taxonomy, or systematics continues up the scale to ever larger groupings, and, in the living world, there are in addition to individuals such higher levels as family, peer groups, and species, communities, societies, and taxa, and so on.

Along with the classificatory stage of scientific development comes the morphological one, in which the original entities are recognized as being, themselves, nonhomogenous and composed of subunits of importance. Thus, individuals are dissected into organs, cells, and molecules. This gives a vertical axis of levels of material entities, each encompassing subordinate ones, from molecules at the lower level of biological interest to world communities or taxa at the upper level. The next stages involve recognition that dynamic or functional units may be as important in one's thinking as are morphological units, and, usually still later, the similar understanding of developmental units.

Each system, then, divides along the horizontal axis into three main rubrics: it has its constant architecture in time, its morphology or "being"; its reversible changes in time, its functioning or "behaving"; and its irreversible changes in time, its development or evolution or history or learning, or "becoming." A table or matrix, with the levels on the ordinate and the three basic properties on the abscissa, forms a most illuminating basis for understanding living systems. I have exemplified the history of science on such a table, spreading up, down, and across from the individual entity, as outlined above (Fig. 1). If the horizontal axis is turned on itself, so that the flat table becomes a vertical cylinder, one can trace spirals of cause and effect from "becoming" at a given level to "being" at the level above, to "behaving" at the level still above. Thus, personal interactions lead to a certain peck order, communication channels, and table of organization, which lead to a certain kind of functioning of a complex organization (Fig. 2). This has been developed at greater length elsewhere.[2]

In the course of evolution of organisms, there has been a profound

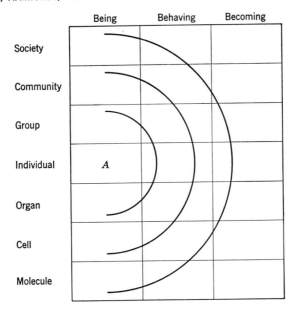

FIG. 1.

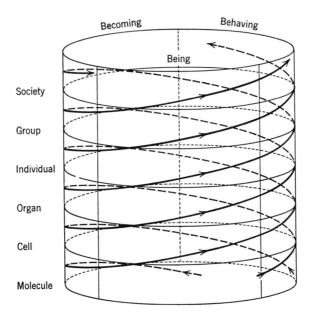

FIG. 2.

shift in the relation of individual to environment. The primitive organisms mostly were sinks for energy and substance, which entered them from the environment and kept them going, while their output of wastes to the environment was utterly unimportant. With the development of greater behavioral capacities, particularly with the ability to use small inputs to trigger the release and mobilization of large energy outputs, organisms gradually came to reverse this relationship and, strikingly in man, have become the source rather than the sink of the important flows between entity and surround. For such triggered control, the pattern of input became vastly more important than the amount, so that information rather than energy received from the environment came to dominate the picture. With larger and larger systems problems, information handling required artificial aids or prostheses, as simple motor action and sensory recognition had required earlier. Fortunately, these have arisen in the computers, the associated mathematics and logic of relationships, the development of on-line man-machine systems for simulation and action, and the other rapidly growing devices for handling the large problems of an epiorganism or a human society. Today, man lives almost exclusively in a sea of information that he has himself created; these newer systems tools and approaches offer the main hope that he will not drown in it.

REFERENCES

1. Gerard, R. W., "Organism, Society, and Science," *Sci. Monthly,* **50** (1940), pp. 340–350, 403–412, 530–535.
2. ———, "The Architecture of Knowledge and Functions," in *Lectures in Experimental Psychiatry* (H. W. Brosin, Ed.), University of Pittsburgh Press, Pittsburgh, 1961, pp. 147–163.

CHAPTER 9

TOWARD APPROXIMATE ANALYSES OF LINEAR DYNAMIC SYSTEMS

WILLIAM K. LINVILL *

All systems must meet up with, soon or later,
A Polynomial Annihilator,
For some damned input, output, chance or state'll
Arrive, of which the consequence is fatal.

K. B.

ABSTRACT

System theory is a component in the problem of the design and engineering of systems and its place is justified in the field by its usefulness in the engineering process. The emergence of a wide range of system problems ranging from system planning to computer-coordinated system design has placed a high premium on engineers who have a broad and thorough grasp of applied mathematics. The greatest need is for those who can handle effectively both the mathematical and physical aspects of the problem. In model building, a thorough grasp of matrices and dynamics is essential. This chapter presents a simple way for engineers to use flow graphs to obtain fairly general and broadly useful results in matrix theory.

INTRODUCTION

It will take some introduction to fit this chapter into the category of general systems theory. Although it presents a few new interpretations of some old mathematical results, it certainly would not be classed as research on mathematical problems. If one interprets theory

* The work in this paper was supported in part by a grant from Westinghouse Electric Corporation.

broadly, then the topics considered here are theoretical in nature. In engineering, theory is a component discipline and must earn its place by meeting some requirement specified by the over-all engineering process. The main focus of my interest is in the invention and design of physical systems to meet some specific practical need. There seem to me to be two kinds of system problems with which engineers are becoming more and more concerned as time passes. They are:

1. Analysis and design of computer-coordinated systems.
2. Long-range planning for systems.

Actually both of these problems or their earlier counterparts have been with us for all of the 20th century. The problems of layout and design of electric power systems are legitimate examples of system engineering. Certainly the problems of laying out an urban transportation system or of a flood control, hydro power, and irrigation project are good system-planning problems. In the past, these problems have been handled by engineers with fairly broad, but not deep, technical interests in applied physics and a strong inclination for engineering economics. Many of the systems problems of the past are still with us, but many more have been added. The rapid growth of technology, particularly in data processing and communication, has made the incidence of technical factors involved in system problems high enough so that the level of training in the physical sciences required for system work has drastically increased. The possibilities of coordination of system components so that they interact constructively have changed the nature of system design from those of preventing interference among parts to providing mutual support among them. This problem is one of interesting proportions to the applied mathematicians and, as the field develops, it is very likely to create a new science of organization.

Our attitude at Stanford has been to get involved in the technical problems of system engineering on a fairly wide spectrum of problems so that we can develop the theory in a way which keeps the theoretical work well coordinated with practical application. Our concern with developing theory "in a vacuum" is that it very often tends to meet so few practical constraints that it is substantially worthless. If one were to do theoretical research independent of practical considerations, one might be better advised to do it as mathematical research where it could fit more adequately into a philosophical framework which had been better tested by the passage of time than our short-term new ideas could be.

To insist on fairly close correlation with practice implies that our range of problems and of theoretical research is not initially as broad as it could otherwise be. To give a description of the fields we are studying, I will list some of the projects now under way in the hope that they orient the reader to the areas to which some of our ideas are relevant. The research projects we are carrying on are:

1. Computer control and coordination of electric power systems.
2. Dynamic scheduling of sequential multiple-service operations. (Steel mill operation, earth-moving in the construction industry.)
3. The use of computers to coordinate programmed learning.
4. Planning for expansion in the electric power industry.
5. Development of overseas markets.
6. Planning for the development of water resources.
7. Planning antimissile defense systems.
8. Man-machine interaction in computer-aided analysis.

Our approach in the University Program is to provide the students with an adequate background in mathematics and physical sciences to tackle the problems encountered in such specific areas as these. Our decision has been to add to the specific mathematics and physics courses several engineering-type courses with applied mathematics slant which will add substantial engineering insight over what would be provided by courses in the mathematics department. These courses in no way substitute for mathematics or physics courses, and the students are encouraged to take much stronger preparation in these areas than usual engineering training commonly provides.

The two kinds of problems in system engineering are model making and optimization. All of system engineering work may be broadly classified into one or both of these two areas. Both areas provide problems of interest to applied mathematicians. Before a problem is mathematically complicated enough to challenge a mathematical specialist, it will have to be studied practically in many aspects so that the less directly involved factors can be eliminated or handled approximately. To be useful, an applied mathematician without practical insight must be given a clearly defined problem with the less relevant factors separated out. To go from a practical situation to such a statement requires a rare mixture of mathematical circumspection and practical insight. Such a mixture is the essence of good system engineering, and problems requiring it cannot be delegated. The system engineer requires a firm mathematical basis for model making and optimization along with an intuitive grasp of the relation of mathematical and physical principles. I have prepared such a correlation in the area of matrices and dynamics. This is only one area. The same approach must be carried out in many areas. Because our practical research is still in early stages, the relevance of all intuitive approaches to practical problems has not been verified and many practically significant ties to the theory have not yet been discovered. Again, it must be remembered that the approach presented here is not intended as a substitute for mathematical appreciation but is an adjunct to bridge the gap between applied mathematics and engineering.

AN ELEMENTARY SCALAR SYSTEM

In relating matrices and dynamics problems to familiar engineering concepts, we do well to look first at the simplest problem we can find which embodies a significant set of general principles. The flow graph of such a system is pictured in Fig. 1.

The feed-forward element is a unit delay which is represented by the transfer function $1/z$. The excitation sequence is e_k and the response sequence is r_k. The feedback link is represented by a simple gain a with no delay.

Since the system is a linear discrete system, it is well to characterize its response to a unit sample applied at the origin ($k = 0$) with zero initial conditions. The excitation-response pair is pictured in Fig. 2. Note the response is a geometric sequence. The value of a for the example pictured is 0.7. The system presented can be described by a simple first-order difference equation given as eq. 1.

$$r_k = e_{k-1} + a r_{k-1} \tag{1}$$

The response of the system to an arbitrary input can be obtained if the input is given by a step-by-step computation. Given e_0 and r_0, one computes r_1. Given r_1 and e_1, one computes r_2. Given r_2 and e_2, one computes r_3, and so on. The system will clearly be stable if $|a|$ is less

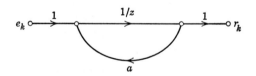

FIG. 1. The flow graph of an elementary system.

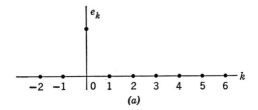

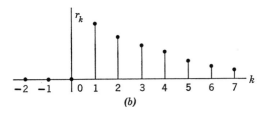

FIG. 2. An excitation-response pair for the system of Fig. 1. (a) The excitation sequence. (b) The response sequence.

than 1, in which case the unit sample response will die out. If Z-transforms are used to describe the system, the transfer function is given by eq. 2.

$$R = \left[\frac{1}{(z - a)}\right] [E + z(e_{-1} + ar_{-1})] \tag{2}$$

Such a system is unusually simple and all its significant properties are seen by inspection. The value of looking at such a system is that it illustrates most of the principles involved in the analysis of a more complicated system.

Had one chosen to analyze a continuous system instead of a discrete system, the delay element of Fig. 1 would simply be replaced by an integrator, as shown in Fig. 3. The description of the system would

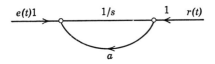

FIG. 3. The flow graph of an elementary continuous system.

be given by eq. 3 and the transfer function by eq. 4. The impulse response is e^{-at} and the system

$$\frac{dr}{dt} = e(t) + ar \tag{3}$$

$$R = \frac{1}{s+a}[E + r(0)] \tag{4}$$

is stable if $Re[a]$ is positive. There is really very little difference between analysis of continuous and discrete systems except discrete systems allow easy solution of paper-and-pencil examples.

AN ELEMENTARY VECTOR SYSTEM

A more interesting set of consequences results when we consider a system having signals which are vectors instead of scalars. The transmission elements are delay elements and matrix operators. The flow graph of such a system is pictured in Fig. 4. The double lines are used to indicate that signals are multidimensional. In some situations it is profitable to view the system with a simple compact matrix notation. In other cases it is more appropriate to use a detailed picture which exhibits all interconnections. Figure 5 shows a two-dimensional system in detail along with an equivalent circuit.

The description of the unit-sample response is now somewhat more complicated than in the case of the scalar system. The excitation vector now has two arbitrary components rather than simply one. Accordingly, to be perfectly general, one would need to find two excitation-response pairs which involved two linearly independent excitation vectors. The two e_0's might well be 1, 0 and 0, 1. An equally good way to represent the excitation-response pair which retains the time relationships and generalizes the geometric sequence of the scalar sys-

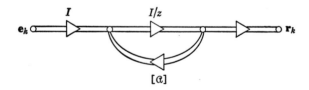

FIG. 4. A flow graph for an elementary vector system.

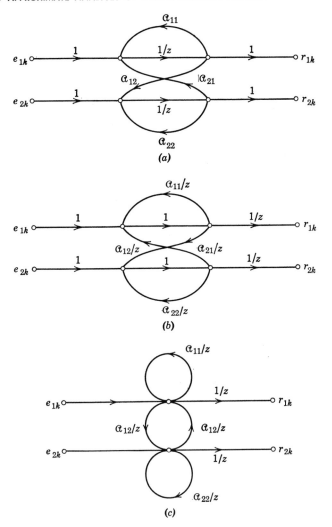

FIG. 5. Detailed flow graphs for two-dimensional vectors. (*a*) Detailed flow graph. (*b*) An equivalent. (*c*) Another equivalent.

tem is to describe the excitation response relation as in Fig. 6. The row matrix **e** represents an arbitrary multiplying factor on the $\mathbf{e}_0$ vector. It is carried as a multiplier to scale the response sequence. A convenient short-hand way to describe the transmission properties of the vector system is to indicate that they are represented by a *geometric matrix sequence* instead of a geometric scalar sequence as in the scalar system.

$k = -2$	$k = -1$	$k = 0$	$k = 1$	$k = 2$	$k = 3$	$k = 4$	$k = 5$	$k = 6$
$\mathbf{e}_k$	0	0	$\mathbf{e}$	0	0	0	0	0	0
$\mathbf{r}_k$	0	0	0	$\mathbf{e}$	$\mathbf{e}[a]$	$\mathbf{e}[a]^2$	$\mathbf{e}[a]^3$	$\mathbf{e}[a]^4$	$\mathbf{e}[a]^5$

FIG. 6. Table of excitation-response vectors.

To complete the picture, we shall draw a few samples from a typical pair of excitation response pairs for a two-dimensional system (Fig. 7). It should be noted in passing that, if the two excitation vectors chosen for the system were the two eigenvectors of the matrix $[a]$, the response sequence would be extremely simply related to the excitation. This situation is pictured in Fig. 8. In this case, note that the excitation vector and its corresponding response vectors are collinear. Each time advance scales the component response by the appropriate eigenvalue.

The excitation response relationship of this situation can be described by a first-order matrix difference equation as given in eq. 5.

$$\mathbf{r}_k = \mathbf{e}_{k-1} + \mathbf{r}_{k-1}[a] \tag{5}$$

Notice that eq. 5 is exactly the matrix equivalent of eq. 1. The use of Z-transforms yields an equivalent to the transfer function relationship in eq. 2. It is given in eq. 6.

$$\mathbf{R} = \{\mathbf{E} + z(\mathbf{e}_{-1} + \mathbf{r}_{-1}[a])\}[Iz - a]^{-1} \tag{6}$$

Whereas the transfer function in the scalar system is $1/(z - a)$ the transfer function in the vector system is the matrix analog, $[Iz - a]^{-1}$.

Recall from the scalar system that the stability of the system depended upon whether the value of a is less than 1. This was the equivalent of whether the poles of the transfer function lie within the unit circle. By referring to Fig. 6, we see that the stability of the vector system is assured if the matrix geometric sequence approaches zero as higher and higher powers are taken. Such will be the case if all eigenvalues of $[a]$ are less than one.

From a transfer function point of view we see in eq. 6 that the poles of the matrix $[Iz - a]^{-1}$ are the zeros of the determinant $|Iz - a|$. But this is exactly the determinant we use to evaluate the eigenvalues. The system poles and the eigenvalues of the characteristic matrix are thus identical!

It should be noted in passing that, if one is given a sequence of excitation vectors $\mathbf{e}_k$ and an initial condition vector $\mathbf{r}_{-1}$, one can compute the response vector sequence $\mathbf{r}_k$ step by step. This ease of computation corresponds to the simplicity of paper-and-pencil exercises with the scalar system.

The ease of handling the vector system of simple structure naturally induces us to ask how general it is. The answer is that any high-order scalar difference equation can be replaced by a vector difference of first order by simply letting each successive sample of the scalar system be a new dimension of the vector system. Then the dimension of the first-order vector system exactly equals the order of the scalar system. This procedure for changing variable is exactly the procedure used to get servosystems into the state variable form.

The foregoing discussion has constituted a quick summary of the analysis of vector systems of simple structure. Since we see that any

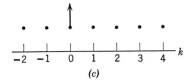

(a)

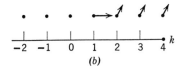

(b)

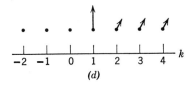

(c)

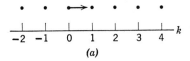

(d)

FIG. 7. Two excitation-response pairs for a two-dimensional system. $[a] = \begin{bmatrix} .5 & .5 \\ .4 & .6 \end{bmatrix}$. (a) Excitation sequence for $e_0 = 1, 0$. (b) Response sequence for $e_0 = 1, 0$. (c) Excitation sequence for $e_0 = 0, 1$. (d) Response sequence for $e_0 = 0, 1$.

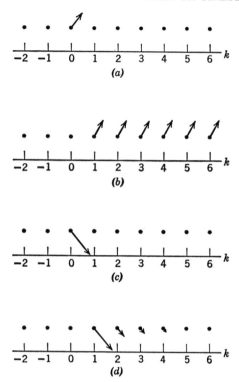

FIG. 8. Two excitation-response pairs for two-dimensional systems (excitation along eigenvectors of $[a]$). (a) Excitation sequence for $e_0 = .0, .5$ ($\lambda = 1$ eigenvector). (b) Response sequence for $e_0 = .0, .5$. (c) Excitation sequence for $e_0 = .5, -.5$ ($\lambda = 0.1$ eigenvector). (d) Response sequence for $e_0 = .5, -.5$.

system can be represented by such a structure, the value of studying the transition matrix $[a]$ to derive properties of the system is clear. Conversely, a good way to study the properties of any matrix $[a]$ is to imbed it in a feedback structure!

We will now take this tack and find that there is indeed a strong union between conventional control theory and matrix theory. For this study it will be valuable to consider simultaneously three forms of the simple flow graph structure we have already presented. We will choose to go back and forth from one to another of these as our discussion progresses. Before we embark on a combined study of the three, let us describe each one in some detail at the outset. The first form is simply the one presented in Fig. 4. Its simple characteristic is that it generates a geometric matrix sequence $[a]^n$ as the transfer operator.

The second form of the flow graph of Fig. 4 is the result of making a partial fraction expansion of $[Iz - a]^{-1}$. For the moment, let us assume that the matrix $[a]$ has simple eigenvalues. Then it is very easy to split $[Iz - a]^{-1}$ in a partial fraction expansion. The resulting form is that expressed in eq. 7.

$$[Iz - a]^{-1} = \frac{R_1}{z - \lambda_1} + \frac{R_2}{z - \lambda_2} + \cdots \frac{R_n}{z - \lambda_n} \tag{7}$$

The R_k's are a set of matrices of constants. By noting that transmissions in parallel add, we can immediately sketch an equivalent to Fig. 4 (see Fig. 9). Note that the transform of the drive is $\mathbf{E}$ if the initial conditions are zero. For nonzero initial conditions, one must modify the excitation as indicated in eq. 6. For all our discussions we will have zero initial conditions for all k less than the k corresponding to earliest excitation, so the initial conditions may be ignored. The particular value of the flow graph presented here is that it automatically splits the response into normal modes. Thus, making partial fraction expansions and changing to normal coordinates must be intimately related.

The third form of the flow graph of Fig. 4 results from changing to normal coordinates. If the response vector at time k is presented in the reference coordinates, then it is described by a row matrix $\mathbf{r}_k$. If it is presented in the normal coordinates, it is described by a different response row matrix $\boldsymbol{\rho}_k$, where $\mathbf{r}_k$ and $\boldsymbol{\rho}_k$ are related by eq. 8.

$$\mathbf{r}_k = \boldsymbol{\rho}_k[P] \tag{8}$$

Each of the rows of the transformation matrix P represents an eigenvector of the transition matrix $[a]$. To go from the reference coordinates

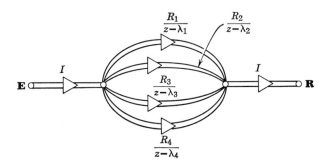

FIG. 9. The partial-fraction equivalent of the vector system of elementary structure.

r_k to the normal coordinates ρ_k, one merely postmultiplies the r_k matrix by $[P]^{-1}$ as in eq. 9.

$$r_k[P]^{-1} = \rho_k \qquad (9)$$

These operations can be interpreted by flow graph representations as is done by the steps indicated in Fig. 10. The value of such a change is actually best realized by comparing the detailed flow graphs in reference coordinates given in Fig. 5 to the detailed flow graph equivalent of Fig. 5 when put in normal coordinates, as shown in Fig. 10b. The result is pictured in Fig. 11.

We now note that all the transmissions involving delays and dynamics have been isolated in the central region and decoupled by changing from reference coordinates to normal coordinates. The transmission through the upper loop corresponds to a term in the partial-fraction expansion of $[Iz - a]^{-1}$ that has a pole at $z = \lambda_1$. The transmission through the lower loop corresponds to a term in the partial-fraction expansion of $[Iz - a]^{-1}$ that has a pole at $z = \lambda_2$. Thus this two-dimensional case was handled as in Fig. 9, and in eq. 7 we can relate R_1 and R_2 to P and P^{-1} as shown in eqs. 10.

$$[R_1] = [P^{-1}] \begin{bmatrix} 1 & 0 \\ 0 & 0 \end{bmatrix} [P] \qquad \text{and} \qquad [R_2] = [P^{-1}] \begin{bmatrix} 0 & 0 \\ 0 & 1 \end{bmatrix} [P] \qquad (10)$$

It follows that the matrices R_1 and R_2 are projection operators which find the projection of an arbitrary input vector e_k on the first and second eigenvectors respectively of the matrix $[a]$.

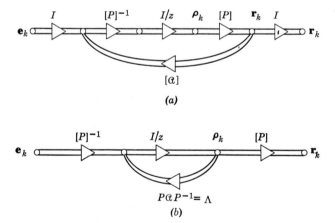

FIG. 10. (a) A change to normal coordinates. (b) An equivalent to (a) but with $[P]^{-1}$ and $[P]$ moved to before and after summing points respectively.

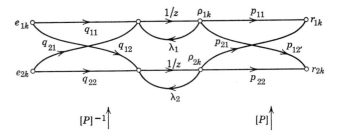

FIG. 11. The elementary system viewed in normal coordinates.

If one refers to Fig. 9, one can see that a unit sample applied to the input e_0 would excite all of the modes unless, of course, it happened to have a zero projection along one of the eigenvectors. The response at the first mode would have an amplitude $e_0[R_1]$, and the ratios of successive samples of response would be λ_1. The response at the second mode would be $e_0[R_2]$, and the ratios of successive samples of the response would be λ_2, and so on. By applying an excitation only along the first eigenvector, one would excite only the first mode. Thus one way to excite selectively various modes would be by selecting the direction of the excitation vector.

By recalling the results of transform analysis of scalar systems, we see another alternative way to selectively excite modes. If an excitation is applied to the input with a transform having a zero at $z = \lambda_1$, then no persistent response from the first mode will be realized. This results because the zero in the transform of the excitation exactly cancels the pole at $z = \lambda_1$ in the transfer function, and in the transform of the response there is no pole at $z = \lambda_1$. This result is illustrated by eqs. 11.

$$\mathbf{R} = \mathbf{e}(z - \lambda_1)\left(\frac{R_1}{z - \lambda_1} + \frac{R_2}{z - \lambda_2} + \frac{R_3}{z - \lambda_3} + \frac{R_4}{z - \lambda_4}\right)$$

$$= \mathbf{e}\left[R_1 + \frac{R_2(z - \lambda_1)}{z - \lambda_2} + \frac{R_3(z - \lambda_1)}{z - \lambda_3} + \frac{R_4(z - \lambda_1)}{z - \lambda_4}\right]$$

(11)

In these equations note that the transform of the excitation is $\mathbf{e}(z - \lambda_1)$. This factor $\mathbf{e}$ is an arbitrary vector which determines the vector direction of the excitation. It is the same $\mathbf{e}$ which was referred to earlier in the discussion of Fig. 6. Of course, if the direction chosen for $\mathbf{e}$ had no projection on one of the eigenvectors, that mode would not be excited regardless of the transform relations. For the moment we will assume that the vector $\mathbf{e}$ is picked so that it has a non-zero projection on all the eigenvectors of $[a]$.

If we examine the terms of eq. 11 we see that the first term corresponds to the transform of a response at $k = 0$ but with no terms thereafter. The other three terms each represent a persistent transient. Thus were we to look at the response at $k = 1$, we would find no response having the vector direction $\mathbf{e}R_1$. There would be response in the directions $\mathbf{e}R_2$, $\mathbf{e}R_3$, and $\mathbf{e}R_4$.

It is instructive to get the response to the signal $\mathbf{e}(z - \lambda_1)$ by inspection of the flow graph of Fig. 4. The signal whose transform is $\mathbf{e}(z - \lambda_1)$ represents a vector $\mathbf{e}$ applied to the system at $k = -1$ and a vector $-\lambda_1\mathbf{e}$ applied to the system at $k = 0$. By superposition, one can evaluate the response of the system at $k = 1$ to each input and then add the result. From the table of Fig. 6 we see that the response at $k = 1$ to the input $-\lambda_1\mathbf{e}$ at $k = 0$ is merely $-\lambda_1\mathbf{e}$. Similarly, the response at $k = 1$ to the input $\mathbf{e}$ at $k = -1$ is merely $\mathbf{e}[a]$. Thus the total response is given by the sum of the two responses or $\mathbf{e}[a - \lambda_1 I]$. By interpretation of the partial-fraction expansion we see that the response of the system at $k = 1$ can have no component along the first eigenvector of $[a]$. But this response is also represented by $\mathbf{e}[a - \lambda_1 I]$. Hence regardless of the direction of $\mathbf{e}$, the response must have no component along the first eigenvector. In matrix terms, the matrix polynomial $[a - \lambda_1 I]$ *annihilates* the space of the first eigenvector. We have just established a direct connection between annihilator polynomials of matrices and zeros in Z-transforms. They amount to the same.

By referring to the table in Fig. 6 one can easily verify that, if one applies an input signal $\mathbf{e}[\alpha_0 z^m + \alpha_1 z^{m-1} + \alpha_2 z^{m-2} + \cdots \alpha_m]$ to a vector system of simple structure, the response at $k = 1$ will be $\mathbf{e}[\alpha_0 a^m + \alpha_1 a^{m-1} + \alpha_2 a^{m-2} + \cdots \alpha_m I]$. Or more compactly, if a signal whose transform is $\mathbf{e}[f(z)]$ is applied to a vector system of simple structure with a transition matrix a, the response at $k = 1$ is $\mathbf{e}[f(a)]$.

Referring back to Fig. 9 and the discussion of eq. 11, we see that, if a signal were applied to the system having a zero for each pole of the system transfer function, then all modes of the response would be annihilated and the total system response would be 0 at $k = 1$. Such an excitation would be $\mathbf{e}(z - \lambda_1)(z - \lambda_2)(z - \lambda_3)(z - \lambda_4) = \mathbf{e}\,\Delta(z)$. From our previous discussion we see that the total response at $k = 1$ would be $\mathbf{e}\{[a - \lambda_1 I][a - \lambda_2 I][a - \lambda_3 I][a - \lambda_4]\}$, or $\mathbf{e}\,\Delta(a)$. Regardless of $\mathbf{e}$, this response must be zero. Hence $\Delta(a) = 0$. This is the famous Cayley-Hamilton theorem which is simply equivalent to saying that, if a system is excited by a signal with zeros to cancel every pole, there is no response after $k = 0$.

By using the approach of Fig. 9 and eq. 11, we see that we can selectively excite any mode of the system by putting in zeros to cancel all poles but one. The scale of the response at that pole can be controlled by the size of **e**. If we can excite any single mode by such a succession of signals, then we can excite all modes simultaneously and independently by merely applying superposition and putting in n signals simultaneously, each of which will selectively excite a single mode. This whole discussion went on independently of the vector **e** except with the tacit understanding that the vector **e** has a nonzero projection on each eigenvector of $[a]$. In particular, the whole system might be excited by a *single input lead*. For example, if one had only a single dimension of the system available at the input, this situation would correspond to $\mathbf{e} = 1, 0, 0, \cdots$ if the available lead were the first. Now we see two extreme ways of selectively exciting modes: if all modes are reachable from the input, that is, if **e** can have all n components nonzero, one can excite modes selectively in one sample of the input; if only one lead is available but if this lead drives all modes, then the modes can be set up selectively in n samples. Obviously, intermediate excitations are possible by using more than one input component and fewer than n samples.

A very great advantage of the flow graph interpretation of annihilator polynomials is that it is directly applicable whether the transition matrix has simple eigenvalues or not. The partial-fraction expansion procedure is exactly the same as that in conventional Fourier or Laplace transforms. The form of the expansion is given by eq. 12.

$$[Iz - a]^{-1} = \frac{R_{11}}{z - \lambda_1} + \frac{R_{12}}{(z - \lambda_1)^2}$$

$$+ \cdots \frac{R_{1m_1}}{(z - \lambda_1)^{m_1}} + \frac{R_{21}}{(z - \lambda_2)} + \frac{R_{22}}{(z - \lambda_2)^2} + \cdots \quad (12)$$

The partial-fraction expansion leads to an equivalent parallel flow graph of the sort given in Fig. 12. Because of the possibility of cancellation of zeros and poles in the form $[Iz - a]^{-1}$, the degree of the denom-

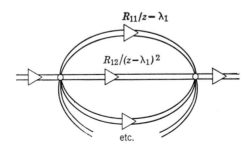

FIG. 12. Part of a flow graph equivalent of the transmission for the multiple-root case.

inator polynomial when all terms of eq. 12 are combined will possibly be less than the value of the determinant $|Iz - a|$. Oftentimes the determinant of the denominator is called $\Delta(z)$. The denominator polynomial which results when terms are collected in eq. 12 will be called $M(z)$. By exactly the same thinking as we went through earlier, it is clear that, if an excitation is applied whose Z-transform is given by eq. 13, there will be no response after $k = 0$, because there will be zeros to cancel all poles.

$$\mathbf{E(z)} = \mathbf{e}M(z) \qquad (13)$$

Of course, if the excitation were $\mathbf{e}\,\Delta(z)$ the response after $k = 0$ would still be 0, but now all responses can be annihilated by a lower degree polynomial $M(z)$. The same kind of thinking done earlier now implies that $M(a) = [0]$. Thus $M(a)$ annihilates the whole space and is referred to as the *minimal polynomial*. The same set of arguments which applied earlier about the place of $\mathbf{e}$ as a vector scale factor still apply.

It turns out that the normal coordinate conversion which applied earlier in the case of simple eigenvalues is now replaced by a Jordan normal form. The response vector $\mathbf{r}_k$ will now be described in terms of its normal coordinates rather than in terms of its reference coordinates. Again we write eq. 8,

$$\mathbf{r}_k = \boldsymbol{\rho}_k[P] \qquad (8)$$

Now each of the rows of the transformation matrix P represents an eigen vector of the transition matrix $[a]$. Again to go from the reference coordinates $\mathbf{r}_k$ to the normal coordinates $\boldsymbol{\rho}_k$, one merely postmultiplies the $\mathbf{r}_k$ matrix by $[P]^{-1}$, as in eq. 9 given earlier.

$$\mathbf{r}_k[P]^{-1} = \boldsymbol{\rho}_k \qquad (9)$$

Again the interpretation of the coordinate change is exactly as was done in Fig. 10 except that $PaP^{-1} = J$, the Jordan form, rather than Λ. The typical form of the Jordan matrix is given in eq. 14.

$$J = \begin{bmatrix} \lambda_1 & 0 & 0 & 0 \\ 1 & \lambda_1 & 0 & 0 \\ 0 & 1 & \lambda_1 & 0 \\ 0 & 0 & 0 & \lambda_2 \end{bmatrix} \qquad (14)$$

Figure 11 is replaced by the analogous Fig. 13 in which the center loops have some couplings. In order to represent the connections, a four-dimensional system will be sketched. The interconnections between the various leads at the input and output are exactly like those of Fig. 11, but are too complicated to draw. Accordingly, they will be represented by a pair of simple blocks. The transfer function for the

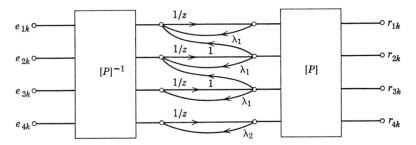

FIG. 13. The elementary vector system viewed in Jordan normal coordinates.

system represented by Fig. 13 will be given by the partial fraction expansion of eq. 15,

$$[Iz - a]^{-1} = \frac{R_{11}}{z - \lambda_1} + \frac{R_{12}}{(z - \lambda_1)^2} + \frac{R_{13}}{(z - \lambda_1)^3} + \frac{R_2}{z - \lambda_2} \qquad (15)$$

It is fairly easy to relate the R's to the $[P]^{-1}$ and $[P]$. By referring to Fig. 13, we see that the only term which has a third order pole at λ_1 is the connection which enters the center part in the third lead and comes out in the first lead. Thus we write eq. 16,

$$R_{13} = [P]^{-1} \begin{bmatrix} 0 & 0 & 0 & 0 \\ 0 & 0 & 0 & 0 \\ 1 & 0 & 0 & 0 \\ 0 & 0 & 0 & 0 \end{bmatrix} [P] \qquad (16)$$

The two terms which involve second-order poles are the connections that enter the center part on the second and third leads and come out on the first and second leads respectively. Thus we write eq. 17,

$$R_{12} = [P]^{-1} \begin{bmatrix} 0 & 0 & 0 & 0 \\ 1 & 0 & 0 & 0 \\ 0 & 1 & 0 & 0 \\ 0 & 0 & 0 & 0 \end{bmatrix} [P] \qquad (17)$$

The three terms that involve first-order poles at λ_1 are the connections which enter and leave the center part on the first, second, and third leads, respectively. Thus we write eq. 18,

$$R_{11} = [P]^{-1} \begin{bmatrix} 1 & 0 & 0 & 0 \\ 0 & 1 & 0 & 0 \\ 0 & 0 & 1 & 0 \\ 0 & 0 & 0 & 0 \end{bmatrix} [P] \qquad (18)$$

R_2 is defined analogously as it was done in eq. 10 for the simpler case presented earlier. There are other more complicated cases to be considered in which we can have two or more chains corresponding to the same eigenvalue. All these cases can be handled in exactly the same way as was done above.

This presentation was given in the belief that work in systems will involve a need for more and more familiarity with matrices and linear vector spaces. Furthermore, we see that these topics are very close to ideas already held by engineers and used widely in practical problems. The ease of relating mathematical results to flow graphs is of great value in deriving models for typical cases. Aside from the obvious uses of these approaches in multivariable control, they often arise in such areas as filtering theory, Markov processes, inventory control, models of learning, and reliability models. The aim is to combine mathematical results with the intuitive insights from an engineering approach to provide useful tools in model making.

CHAPTER 10

INVARIANT IMBEDDING
AND THE ANALYSIS
OF PROCESSES

ROBERT KALABA

My mind's not adequately nimble
To catch the Kalabistic Symbol:
I thought Invariant Imbedding
Was found Sequential to a Wedding!

K. B.

SUMMARY

Many of the processes considered in modern physics and control theory lead, from the mathematical viewpoint, to nonlinear two-point boundary-value problems. These problems are difficult to treat computationally and analytically. A goal of the theory of invariant imbedding is to provide a systematic technique for converting these boundary-value problems into initial-value problems through use of appropriate variables and the employment of functional equation techniques.

A particle multiplication process is considered for illustrative purposes. The classical equations and the invariant imbedding equations are derived and various interconnections are discussed.

INTRODUCTION

One of the most important features of systems is that they undergo processes. Thus, it is that a general theory of systems must concern itself with the theory of processes. The aim of this chapter is to provide an introduction to some recent developments in the theory of processes.

Customarily, when studying a particular process, we focus our attention on it and attempt to discern those properties which are of interest to us. For example, we may describe the state of a system S by means of a vector p, which is viewed as a point in a phase space. The local properties of the process are given by specifying that a system in a state p at time n will be in state q at time $n + 1$. This is symbolized by writing

$$q = T(p, n) \tag{1}$$

Here we are assuming that the process is deterministic and that cause and effect are known. If the initial state is c and if the state at time n is p_n, then the process is described by the equations

$$p_0 = c \tag{2}$$

$$p_{n+1} = T(p_n, n) \qquad n = 0, 1, 2, \cdots \tag{3}$$

We might, for example, wish to determine whether the system remains in a certain region of phase space over all time or not.

One of the key conceptual tools for studying such processes, which are viewed as sequences of transformations of the state of the system, is the observation that the state at time n is a function of the initial state c and the time n, i.e.,

$$p_n = f(c, n) \tag{4}$$

Furthermore, this function $f(c, n)$ has a semigroup[1] property expressed by the equation

$$f(c, m + n) = f(f(c, n), m) \tag{5}$$

This is a symbolic representation of the fact that the state at time $m + n$, the initial state having been c, can be viewed as having been attained by letting n units of time pass, so that the system is transformed into the state $f(c, n)$, and then, considering this as a new initial state, letting an additional m units of time pass. Notice that use of this principle leads us to consider not only the single process of duration $m + n$ and initial condition c but also a class of processes of arbitrary duration and arbitrary initial condition.

In essence, invariant imbedding is a generalization of this concept. To study a particular process, we imbed that process in an appropriate class of processes. Then we express the relationships among the properties of the members of the class. These relations then constitute an analytical description of the processes. In this way we are frequently able to forge new tools for their analytic and computational study. As a rule this leads to the employment of other variables such as length or energy, in addition to the classical one, time, as the semigroup variable.

A discussion of the mathematical treatment of processes, including stochastic, adaptive, and control aspects, can be found in Ref. 2. A discussion of invariant imbedding with applications to neutron transport theory, multiple scattering, diffusion, etc., is given in Ref. 3 where references to the work of Ueno, Redheffer, Preisendorfer, and others will be found. Basic references to the pioneering efforts of S. Chandrasekhar can be found in Ref. 4. Our aim is to show how boundary-value problems can be transformed into initial-value problems, prompted, in part, by the desire to make it easier to bring the power of modern digital computers to bear on significant classes of problems.

In subsequent sections we shall illustrate these general remarks by considering a particle multiplication process. The physical background is provided, the standard description of the process is presented, and then the treatment via invariant imbedding is indicated. Various interconnections are discussed, and some computational and analytical aspects are illuminated. There are immediate applications to analytical dynamics and automatic control theory. The discussion is intended to be self-contained.

THE CLASSICAL TRANSPORT EQUATIONS [3]

Let us consider a particle process which takes place within a thin tube. The tube, assumed homogeneous, extends along a t-axis from $t = 0$ to $t = T$. At the right end, $t = T$, a steady stream of c particles per unit time is incident on the tube, and at the end $t = 0$ a stream of w particles per unit time is incident on the tube. Within the rod, the particles interact with one another and with the material of which the rod is constructed. The flows within the tube are described by the functions $u(t)$ and $v(t)$, where

$$u(t) = \text{the number of particles per second} \atop \text{passing the point } t \text{ and traveling to} \atop \text{the right} \qquad (6)$$

and

$$v(t) = \text{the number of particles per second} \atop \text{passing the point } t \text{ and traveling to} \atop \text{the left} \qquad (7)$$

$$0 \leq t \leq T \qquad (8)$$

The interactions which take place are described by assuming that, when a flow u to the right and a flow v to the left are incident on a section of tube of length Δ, the increment in the flow to the right is $F(u, v)\Delta + o(\Delta)$, and the increment in the flow to the left is $G(u, v)\Delta + o(\Delta)$. Consequently, we may write the equations

$$u(t + \Delta) - u(t) = F(u(t), v(t))\Delta + o(\Delta) \tag{9}$$

$$v(t) - v(t + \Delta) = G(u(t), v(t))\Delta + o(\Delta) \tag{10}$$

where, as usual, $o(\Delta)$ is a function of Δ having the property that

$$\lim_{\Delta \to 0} \frac{o(\Delta)}{\Delta} = 0 \tag{11}$$

Upon dividing eqs. 9 and 10 by Δ and letting Δ tend to zero, we find the relations

$$\frac{du}{dt} = F(u, v) \tag{12}$$

$$-\frac{dv}{dt} = G(u, v) \tag{13}$$

Furthermore, in view of the assumptions made concerning the flows that are incident on the tube, we have the boundary conditions

$$v(T) = c \tag{14}$$

$$u(0) = w \tag{15}$$

In this manner we are led, along classical lines, to study the two-point boundary-value problem of eqs. 12 through 15. Nonlinear two-point boundary-value problems are known to be quite intractable, both analytically and computationally.[5]

THE REFLECTION AND TRANSMISSION FUNCTIONS [6]

To apply the idea of invariant imbedding to the particle process discussed earlier, we consider the class of processes taking place in identical homogeneous tubes of lengths $T \geqq 0$, subject to incident fluxes, at the right end, of $c \geqq 0$. The flux incident on the left end is held fixed at a particular value w. The physical situation suggests that we consider the fluxes which emerge from the right and left ends of the various tubes, which we call the "reflected" and the "transmitted" fluxes. Note that the reflected flux which emerges from the tube of length T, due to an incident flux c on the right end, is a function of c and T. Since there is a constant flux w which is incident on the left ends of the tubes, it is true that the fluxes emerging from the tube are dependent on w, but we suppress this dependence since it plays no real role in our considerations. The reflected flux is denoted by

$$r = r(c, T) \tag{16}$$

Similarly, we denote the transmitted flux by

$$\tau = \tau(c, T) \tag{17}$$

First we observe that the fluxes that emerge from a rod of zero length are known, namely,

$$r(c, 0) = w \tag{18}$$

$$\tau(c, 0) = c \tag{19}$$

Next we set about relating the transmitted and reflected fluxes for rods of neighboring lengths; more precisely, we express the flux reflected from rods of length $T + \Delta$ in terms of the flux reflected from rods of length T. Our basic relation is

$$r(c, T + \Delta) = r(c + G(r, c)\Delta, T) + F(r, c)\Delta + o(\Delta) \tag{20}$$

This equation expresses the fact that the flux reflected from a rod of length $T + \Delta$, due to an incident flux c, consists of three parts:

1. Flux reflected from a rod of length T, due to an input flux c, which is modified by passage through a section of length Δ, and so is of strength $c + G(r, c)\Delta + o(\Delta)$.
2. An increment in the flux to the right due to incident fluxes of strengths r and c on a tube of length Δ.
3. Fluxes proportional to the second and higher powers of Δ.

Upon letting Δ tend to zero in eq. 20, we arrive at the desired equation

$$r_T = G(r, c)r_c + F(r, c) \tag{21}$$

where the subscripts denote partial derivatives.

In general eq. 21 is a first-order nonlinear partial differential equation. Since it is linear in the partial derivatives r_T and r_c, it is referred to as a quasilinear partial differential equation.[7] It is to be solved for the reflection function

$$r = r(c, T) \tag{22}$$

subject to the initial condition in eq. 3.

In a similar manner we see that the transmission function $\tau(c, T)$ satisfies the relation

$$\tau(c, T + \Delta) = \tau(c + G(r, c)\Delta, T) + o(\Delta) \qquad (23)$$

In the limit, as Δ tends to zero, this becomes

$$\tau_T = G(r, c)\tau_c \qquad (24)$$

In addition, the transmission function $\tau = \tau(c, T)$ is subject to the initial condition in eq. 19.

Thus we have succeeded in relating the reflection and transmission properties of tubes of neighboring lengths and incident fluxes to each other. In addition, the transmission and reflection properties of a tube of zero length are known. In this manner we may determine the functions $r(c, T)$ and $\tau(c, T)$ computationally for a desired set of values of the variables c and T.

DETERMINATION OF THE INTERNAL FLUXES IN TERMS OF THE REFLECTED AND TRANSMITTED FLUXES

First let us note that if the function $r(c, T)$ is known, then the boundary-value problem posed earlier is, in effect, transformed into an initial-value problem. For at the right end of the rod both the flux traveling to the left

$$v(T) = c \qquad (25)$$

and the flux traveling to the right

$$u(T) = r(c, T) \qquad (26)$$

are known. However, even more may be said.

Consider an interior point t, where the two fluxes are $u(t)$ and $v(t)$. We may consider that a flux $v(t)$ is incident on a rod of length t, giving rise to a reflected flux $u(t)$; i.e.,

$$u(t) = r(v(t), t) \qquad (27)$$

Furthermore, making use of the transmission function, we note that under these conditions the flux emerging from the left end of the tube, $v(0) = b$, is

$$b = \tau(v(t), t) \qquad (28)$$

If now the eqs. 27 and 28 are solved for u and v in terms of t, b, and w, then we shall have obtained a general solution of the original system of nonlinear differential equations. Though these observations are evident on physical grounds, we can easily verify that, if $u(t)$ and $v(t)$ are two functions that satisfy the eqs. 27 and 28, where $r(c, T)$ and $\tau(c, T)$ are the reflection and transmission functions which satisfy eqs. 21 and 24, then the functions $u(t)$ and $v(t)$ satisfy the original non-linear transport equations. In more picturesque language, we may say that a knowledge of the reflection and transmission functions enables us to determine the fluxes within the tube.

Differentiation of eq. 28 with respect to t yields the relation

$$0 = \tau_v \frac{dv}{dt} + \tau_t \tag{29}$$

Upon comparison with eq. 24, we see that

$$-\frac{dv}{dt} = G(u, v) \tag{30}$$

provided that τ_r and τ_t are finite and

$$\tau_v \neq 0 \tag{31}$$

Next we differentiate eq. 27 with respect to t which yields

$$\frac{du}{dt} = r_v \frac{dv}{dt} + r_t = -r_v G + r_t \tag{32}$$

Comparison with eq. 21 then shows that

$$\frac{du}{dt} = F(u, v) \tag{33}$$

Thus our assertion is established.

Let us note that the assumption

$$\tau_v \neq 0 \tag{34}$$

is a reasonable one, stating that the transmitted flux is not independent of the incident flux. Furthermore, the constants b and w have the physical interpretations

$$u(0) = r(v(0), 0) = w \tag{35}$$

$$b = \tau(v(0), 0) = v(0) \tag{36}$$

AN ILLUSTRATIVE EXAMPLE

As an illustration, consider a neutron multiplication process in which a particle traversing a section of a homogeneous tube of length h has a probability of $ah + o(h)$ of being absorbed by the medium. Upon absorption, the original particle disappears and is replaced by two daughter particles, one traveling in each direction. The tube is of length T, and a flux of average strength c is incident on the right end of the tube and no flux is incident on the left end. In this case it is easy to see that the equations for the average internal fluxes are [8]

$$u(t + h) = u(t) + ahv(t) + o(h) \tag{37}$$

$$v(t) = v(t + h) + ahu(t) + o(h) \tag{38}$$

which become, upon letting h tend to zero,

$$\frac{du}{dt} = av \tag{39}$$

$$-\frac{dv}{dt} = au \tag{40}$$

The boundary conditions are

$$u(0) = 0 \qquad v(T) = c \tag{41}$$

Since

$$F(u, v) = av \tag{42}$$

and

$$G(u, v) = au \tag{43}$$

the equations for the reflected and transmitted fluxes are

$$r_T = ac + arr_c \tag{44}$$

and

$$\tau_T = ar\tau_c \tag{45}$$

In view of the linearity of eqs. 39 and 40, and on physical grounds, we expect that the reflected flux will be proportional to the incident flux c,

$$r(c, T) = R(T)c \tag{46}$$

If we substitute this expression into eq. 44, we find

$$\frac{dR}{dT}c = ac + aR^2c \tag{47}$$

or

$$\frac{dR}{dT} = a(1 + R^2) \tag{48}$$

an ordinary differential equation for the reflection coefficient $R(T)$. For an initial condition we have

$$R(0) = 0 \tag{49}$$

The function $R(T)$ can be found explicitly and is

$$R(T) = \tan aT \tag{50}$$

Thus for the reflection function $r(c, T)$ we have

$$r(c, T) = c \tan aT \tag{51}$$

This is an interesting formula in itself and shows that, if the length of the tube is sufficiently great, $\pi/2a$ to be exact, then the reflected flux becomes infinite. Thus the "critical length" of the tube is

$$T_{\text{crit}} = \frac{\pi}{2a} \tag{52}$$

In a similar manner we find that

$$\tau(c, T) = c \sec aT \tag{53}$$

To find the internal fluxes, we use the integration theory sketched above. First we write

$$u = v \tan at \tag{54}$$

$$b = v \sec at \tag{55}$$

Upon solving for u and v we find

$$v(t) = b \cos at \tag{56}$$

$$u(t) = b \sin at \tag{57}$$

the solutions of eqs. 39, 40, and 41.

RIGOROUS DERIVATION OF THE EQUATIONS FOR THE REFLECTED AND TRANSMITTED FLUXES [9]

In earlier sections we showed how to deduce the equations for the reflected and transmitted fluxes using a physical argument. It is important, though, to have a purely mathematical procedure. In fact, as I. Busbridge points out,[10]

The application of these (invariance) principles is not easy and until a precise statement is given of the physical conditions which are sufficient to ensure their truth, any solution based on these ought to be verified in another way.

In this section we shall show how to deduce the equations for the reflected and transmitted fluxes from the equations for the internal fluxes in a purely mathematical manner. We shall see that the essential feature is the uniqueness of the solution of the linear perturbation equations of the internal flux equations. The basic idea behind the discussion is that there is basically one set of perturbation equations regardless of what is varied.

Let us consider the equations

$$\frac{du}{dt} = F(u, v) \qquad u(0) = 0 \tag{58}$$

$$-\frac{dv}{dt} = G(u, v) \qquad v(T) = c \tag{59}$$

In addition, we consider the same equations for the functions $U(t)$ and $V(t)$ on the interval $t = 0$ to $t = T + h$, with the same boundary conditions,

$$\frac{dU}{dt} = F(U, V) \qquad U(0) = 0 \tag{60}$$

$$-\frac{dV}{dt} = G(U, V) \qquad V(T + h) = c \tag{61}$$

We may refer these equations to the interval $t = 0$ to $t = T$ by noting that

$$V(T) = c - V'(T)h = c + G(U(T), V(T))h \tag{62}$$
$$= c + G(u(T), v(T))h$$

In the above equations we have suppressed all terms involving powers of h higher than the first. For ease in writing we shall continue to do this throughout the section. Next we introduce the perturbation functions $w(t)$ and $x(t)$ via the relations

$$U(t) = u(t) + w(t)h \tag{63}$$

$$V(t) = v(t) + x(t)h \tag{64}$$

which hold for $0 \leq t \leq T$.

If we write

$$U(T + h) = U(T) + U'(T)h$$
$$= u(T) + w(T)h + F(u(T), v(T))h \tag{65}$$

and

$$V(0) = v(0) + x(0)h \tag{66}$$

we see that we must study $w(T)$ and $x(0)$ in more detail.

We know that the functions $w(t)$ and $x(t)$ satisfy the linear perturbation equations

$$\frac{dw}{dt} = F_u(u, v)w + F_v(u, v)x \qquad (67)$$

$$-\frac{dx}{dt} = G_u(u, v)w + G_v(u, v)x \qquad (68)$$

As boundary conditions we have

$$w(0) = 0 \qquad (69)$$

and

$$x(T) = G(u(T), v(T)) \qquad (70)$$

The second condition follows from eq. 62. In addition, we see that, if we regard the functions $u(t)$ and $v(t)$ as functions of the parameter c, then

$$\frac{d}{dt} u_c = F_u(u, v)u_c + F_v(u, v)v_c \qquad (71)$$

$$-\frac{d}{dt} v_c = G_u(u, v)u_c + G_v(u, v)v_c \qquad (72)$$

Furthermore, the functions u_c and v_c satisfy the boundary conditions

$$u_c(0) = 0 \qquad (73)$$

$$v_c(T) = 1 \qquad (74)$$

If we now assume that there is a unique solution of eqs. 67 and 68, subject to the conditions of eqs. 69 and 70 on the interval $[0, T]$, then we have the desired results

$$w = G(u(T), v(T))u_c \qquad (75)$$

and

$$x = G(u(T), v(T))v_c \qquad (76)$$

For T sufficiently small this assumption is certainly justified.

Equation 65 now becomes

$$U(T + h) = u(T) + u_cG(u(T), v(T))h + F(u(T), v(T))h \qquad (77)$$

Upon writing

$$u(T) = r(c, T) \qquad (78)$$

and letting h tend to zero, we find

$$\frac{\partial r}{\partial T} = G(r, c) \frac{\partial r}{\partial c} + F(r, c) \qquad (79)$$

This is the desired equation for the reflection function. Equation 66 becomes

$$V(0) = v(0) + G(u(T), v(T))v_c h]_{t=0} \qquad (80)$$

This leads to our equation for the transmission function

$$\frac{\partial r}{\partial T} = G(r, c)\frac{\partial \tau}{\partial c} \qquad (81)$$

In the above manner we see how the mathematical relations between the equations for the transmitted and reflected fluxes and those for the internal fluxes arise. These relationships may be illuminated from a different mathematical viewpoint, as is shown in Ref. 11. There, for linear systems, the equations for the internal fluxes can be considered as arising as Euler equations for a certain quadratic variational problem. The equations for the reflected and transmitted fluxes arise upon applying the principle of optimality [5] to the same quadratic variational problem. Lastly, let us note that results of the foregoing nature contain the variational formulas for one-dimensional Green's functions and for the characteristic functions and characteristic values.[12] The same method applies to time-dependent and other transport processes.

DISCUSSION

A given physical process can be considered from various mathematical viewpoints. It is to be expected that certain properties will be more apparent from some viewpoints than from others. Frequently, the classical derivations lead to boundary-value problems which are difficult to treat, especially from the computational viewpoint. One way of overcoming these difficulties is through use of the functional equation techniques of invariant imbedding, as we have seen.

Many of the classical equations of mathematical physics [7] as well as those of modern automatic control theory [13] arise in the form of Euler equations associated with the minimization of certain functionals. As a rule, boundary conditions either are given or arise in the form of free boundary conditions. Thus it is that a major problem in all of modern physics and control theory is the resolution of boundary-value problems. Application of invariant imbedding to dynamics can be found in Refs. 14 and 15. An alternative to the usual Hamilton-Jacobi theory is provided.

The considerations of this paper are readily generalized to systems of equations of order higher than two.[6] They are also applicable to the differential-integral equations which arise in neutron transport theory [16] and radiative transfer.[17]

From the conceptual viewpoint, let us point out that the establishing of existence and uniqueness of solution for nonlinear two-point boundary-value problems is difficult. Invariant imbedding offers one avenue of approach.[18] The close conceptual relation between invariant imbedding and dynamic programming is evident.[5]

Finally let us note that a direct computational attack on nonlinear two-point boundary-value problems is possible via quasilinearization.[19]

REFERENCES

1. Hille, E., and R. Phillips, *Functional Analysis and Semi-Groups*, American Mathematical Society, Providence, R. I., 1957.
2. Bellman, R., and R. Kalaba, "Dynamic Programming and Adaptive Processes," *IRE Trans. on Automatic Control*, **AC-5** (1960), pp. 5–10.
3. Bellman, R., R. Kalaba, and G. M. Wing, "Invariant Imbedding and Mathematical Physics—I: Particle Processes," *J. Math. Phys.*, **1** (1960), pp. 280–308.
4. Chandrasekhar, S., *Radiative Transfer*, Dover Publications, New York, 1960.
5. Bellman, R., *Adaptive Control Processes: A Guided Tour*, Princeton University Press, Princeton, N. J., 1961.
6. Bellman, R., R. Kalaba, and G. M. Wing, "Invariant Imbedding and the Reduction of Two-Point Boundary-Value Problems to Initial-Value Prroblems," *Proc. Nat. Acad. Sci. USA*, **46** (1960), pp. 1646–1649.
7. Courant, R., and D. Hilbert, *Methods of Mathematical Physics*, Vol. 2, Interscience Publishers, New York, 1962.
8. Bellman, R., and R. Kalaba, "Transport Theory and Invariant Imbedding," in *Nuclear Reactor Theory*, American Mathematical Society, Providence, R. I., 1961.
9. Bellman, R., and R. Kalaba, "On the Fundamental Equations of Invariant Imbedding," *Proc. Nat. Acad. Sci. USA*, **47** (1961), pp. 336–338.
10. Busbridge, I., *The Mathematics of Radiative Transfer*, Cambridge University Press, London, 1960.
11. Bellman, R., R. Kalaba, and G. M. Wing, "Invariant Imbedding and Variational Principles in Transport Theory," *Bull. Amer. Math. Soc.*, **67** (1961), pp. 396–399.
12. Bellman, R., and R. S. Lehman, "Functional Equations in the Theory of Dynamic Programming—X: Resolvents, Characteristic Functions and Values," *Duke Math. J.*, **27** (1960), pp. 55–70.
13. Pontryagin, L., et al., *The Mathematical Theory of Optimal Processes*, Interscience Publishers, New York, 1962.
14. Bellman, R., and R. Kalaba, "A Note on Hamilton's Equations and Invariant Imbedding," *Quart. of Appl. Math.*, vol. 21 (1963), pp. 166–168.

15. Bellman, R., and R. Kalaba, *Invariant Imbedding and the Integration of Hamilton's Equations*, The RAND Corporation, RM-3538-PR, February 1963.
16. Wing, G. M., *An Introduction to Transport Theory*, John Wiley and Sons, New York, 1962.
17. Bellman, R., R. Kalaba, and M. Prestrud, *Invariant Imbedding and Radiative Transfer in Slabs of Finite Thickness*, Elsevier Publishing Co., New York, 1963.
18. Bellman, R., R. Kalaba, and G. M. Wing, "Dissipation Functions and Invariant Imbedding, I," *Proc. Nat. Acad. Sci. USA*, **46** (1960), pp. 1145–1147.
19. Kalaba, R., "On Nonlinear Differential Equations, The Maximum Operation and Monotone Convergence," *J. Math. and Mech.*, **8** (1959), pp. 519–574.

CHAPTER 11

SYSTEM CAUSALITY AND SIGNAL PREDICTABILITY

RUDOLF F. DRENICK

INTRODUCTION

This chapter deals with a problem in the theory of physical systems, a problem which is, by all indications, quite a fundamental one. It is mainly concerned with the one property that all physical systems have in common, namely, that of being causal. Accordingly, it should lead to assertions which are about as general as can be made about physical systems, and only about these. Being general, the assertions are necessarily also somewhat weak, and their immediate value is of a conceptual rather than of a practical nature. This need not be all, however. On the contrary, as far as one can now determine it, the problem will carry important implications into several related fields, such as control and communications theory. But it is an unsolved problem.

The purpose of this chapter is to describe the problem briefly and qualitatively, to state the solution that is now anticipated for it, and to sketch one of its applications, namely, to the field of prediction theory. The main purpose of this chapter is to call attention to the problem. It has not received the interest which, in my opinion, it deserves. If it had, it might be solved by now, and an exasperating road block would thus have been removed which now stands in the way of the development of a general theory of physical systems.

THE PROBLEM AND ITS BACKGROUND

I will discuss the general theory of physical systems in the sense of the term used by Zadeh (see Chapter 3) and, as stated above, particularly a property that all such systems have in common, namely, that of being causal. That is to say, the output of such a system at

157

any one time can depend only on the input up to and including that time but not on the input beyond that time. This property is considered so basic that "physical" and "causal" are often equated, and noncausal systems are viewed as mere mathematical constructs. This standpoint may be somewhat extreme in practice but, at any rate, system causality is one of the main ingredients of the problem to be discussed below.

A second ingredient is the following. It is also pointed out by Zadeh (Chapter 3) that the output of many physical systems is unspecified even when the input is completely known until certain complementary data are supplied concerning the state of the system at the start of its operation. These data are often called the "initial state" of the system. Now it is a curious and often overlooked fact that in some systems the initial state becomes less and less significant the further in the past the system operation is initiated, while in others it does not. In other words, in some systems the initial state is what we may call "asymptotically irrelevant" while in others it is not.

Finite-state machines are typically of the latter type. The output of such a device will, in general, depend equally strongly on the initial state, no matter how remote the starting time of the operation. On the other hand, most systems with continuous-state spaces, such as linear networks and most of the conventional control and communications systems, have initial states which are asymptotically irrelevant. They tend to "forget" the initial state. This is an important property because these types of systems are usually required to convert input into output in a one-one fashion, at least in the long run. A conversion in which the output reflects not only the input but also the initial state is highly undesirable, and the quicker the memory of the latter dies out, the better. (In fact, a failure to do so implies another, even more undesirable, property in many systems, namely, that of instability. An unstable system is for all purposes useless.)

Asymptotic irrelevance of the initial state is therefore essential for a one-to-one conversion of input to output. For this reason, it is a property that deserves some study. What is more, it is a property which seems fairly intimately connected with causality, so much so that the studies of the latter have so far always involved the former.

Such studies have up to now been directed towards the following issue. One might expect, from what has been said, that the operation on some set of input signals by a noncausal system should induce in it some tell-tale symptom which would be indicative of its having been operated on in an unreal fashion and which would not be present otherwise. One might expect the syndrome to be aggravated in some way if the system's initial state is not irrelevant asymptotically. The search for such symptoms and the proof of their infallibility have, in fact, been the central problems in the area of study so far. They are also the topic of this chapter.

Of some additional interest may be the fact that up to now the problem has been attacked chiefly within the framework of probability theory. It may or may not be necessary to do so but, since this is the situation at present, it may be well to explain briefly the form that the problem takes when formulated probabilistically, particularly since in this form some features emerge which are missing otherwise.

THE PROBABILISTIC APPROACH

In the probabilistic approach to systems problems of all kinds, one usually begins by defining (among other things) a probability measure on the set of all allowable input signals, and makes it into what we will call a "random signal" here. One then studies the change that the measure undergoes as the input random signal is transformed into the output by the system under consideration. This, it turns out, is almost as good as studying the system itself. For the change in a probability measure conveys a great deal of information concerning the system that is responsible for it. In fact, in many cases, it conveys all the information really needed.

In the problem under discussion here, it is quite a special piece of information which is primarily desired concerning the system, namely, whether or not it is causal. It stands to reason that a noncausal system, that is, one lacking the basic property of all physical systems, should induce in its output measure some striking feature which would indicate its having been generated by a noncausal operation. This seems to be, in fact, the case. The feature involves more especially the presence of a perfectly predictable component in the output when none was present in the input.

A perfectly predictable component is a signal, embedded in another, which has some rather singular properties. It is a signal whose future can be completely extrapolated from its past and which, therefore, is, in a sense, not even a bona-fide random signal. As a matter of fact, if one takes the point of view of Shannon's communication theory, it is a signal that carries no information. The extrapolation of a perfectly predictable signal can be executed at any time, past, present, or future, and it can in particular be executed arbitrarily far in the past. Therefore, one can say (and does say) that the origin of a perfectly predictable signal antedates time.

As stated above, the presence of a perfectly predictable component "seems" to be the mark of a noncausal operation, but the fact of the matter is that it is not known whether or not this is always true. It can only safely be said that, according to all indications, a close tie exists between noncausality in a system and perfect predictability of some of its output, and that one can serve as a necessary and sufficient condition for the presence of the other.

To be a little more specific, suppose that two random signals are given, one designated as the input to some system, causal or not, and the other as the output. Both are assumed to go back to time $(-\infty)$, so that the initial state of the system is irrelevant if it is asymptotically irrelevant in the first place. The input signal is assumed to contain no perfectly predictable components, but the output signal may contain one. The problem is then this: Is it correct to say that the signal designated as the input will always be convertible into the given output by some causal system and in a one-to-one fashion, provided the output does not contain a perfectly predictable component, but that such a conversion is impossible if it does?

The answer to this question would evidently constitute a theorem of consequence. Unfortunately, as we have said before, a proof of it is still outstanding. Proofs have, however, been supplied for a rather large class of special cases, so large, in fact, that the outlines of the general theorem already seem quite clearly discernible and can be conjectured with considerable assurance. Accordingly, the situation is, in fact, more complicated than our question above indicates.

As will become clear presently, it is no essential restriction in dealing with this problem to standardize the input. It is customary to use as the standard input a random signal often called white noise, that is, a signal all of whose instantaneous samples are statistically independent. White noise, by its definition, contains no perfectly predictable component. It also develops that one must distinguish between signals—white noise and others—whose samples can assume only a discrete set of values (such as the numbers 0 and 1, or the decimal digits, or the integers), and those which can range over a continuum (such as the numbers between 0 and 1, or those between $-\infty$ and $+\infty$). We shall call the first type a discrete signal and the range of its values its "alphabet," following Shannon's terminology. The other will be called a continuous signal. Of course, whether discrete or continuous, it will be further necessary to distinguish between signals that do, and those that do not, contain a perfectly predictable component.

In these terms, it is possible to state what the assertions of the above-mentioned theorem are likely to be. They will be roughly the following:

1. Every random signal can be decomposed into two components, one that can be, and one that cannot be, generated from white noise by causal systems. However, the component that cannot be so generated is perfectly predictable.

2. The white noise mentioned in assertion 1 must be a continuous signal even if the desired output signal is discrete.

3. The conversion from white noise to the desired output signal is one-to-one unless the latter contains a discrete component in which case it is many-to-one. In any case, the system executing the conversion must have an asymptotically irrelevant initial state.

This result, conjectural as it is, has two main implications and a number of subsidiary ones. Speaking qualitatively, it shows first of all that white noise of the kind described under assertion 2 can serve as a sort of universal raw material for the generation of signals. Furthermore, causal systems whose initial states are asymptotically irrelevant can be used for this purpose and will generate any given signal in a one-to-one fashion except for its perfectly predictable component (if any). In Shannon's terminology, it is the information-bearing portion of a signal that can be causally generated from white noise, whereas the one that is devoid of information cannot.

Another implication of this theorem (assuming that it is true) is that, barring the presence of both discrete and perfectly predictable components, a given signal cannot only be generated from, but can also be reconverted to, white noise, and that either or both operations can be carried out in a one-one fashion by causal systems whose initial states are asymptotically irrelevant. White noise of the kind described in assertion 2 can, therefore, serve not only as the raw material for other signals but it can act also as the ultimate final product, and for that matter, as a universal intermediary for the conversion of one signal into another.

The theorem, therefore (still assuming that it is true), makes some fairly sweeping statements concerning the interconvertibility of information-bearing signals by means of physical systems, a fact which, in my opinion, makes it quite fundamental in a general theory of systems. It may accordingly be useful to review how much of it has been proved so far.

The theorem has been known for some time to hold in the case of a special class of random signals, namely, the Gaussian. It was proved by Wold,[3] and the procedure for resolving such a signal into its information-bearing and its perfectly predictable components has come to be known as the Wold decomposition. There exists an extremely seductive generalization of this procedure to non-Gaussian signals, one which utilizes an observation made in another context by Levy.[4] Unfortunately, this generalization is wrong, a fact which was discovered by Rosenblatt[5] who supplied an ingenious counter example. The most general case of the decomposition so far achieved has been reported by Hansen.[2] A necessary and sufficient condition relevant to this problem is also known.[1]

Assertion 3 of our unproved "main result" makes a curious special case of discrete signals. In fact, so does assertion 2, on closer inspection, for it points out that discrete white noise is not, in general, a useful raw material and, by implication, discrete-state machines are not in general useful for the conversion of such noise into other discrete signals, or vice versa. This is actually the case.

The situation is more particularly the following, as far as can be ascertained at this writing.

a. A discrete signal cannot, in general, be generated from discrete white noise, nor can it be converted to it in a one-one fashion by causal discrete-state machines, not even if their alphabets are the same and if perfectly predictable components are absent in both. In fact, conversion may not even be possible by noncausal machines.

b. If a discrete signal is known to have been generated from discrete white noise by a causal machine, then it can be causally reconverted to that noise only if the machine had an asymptotically irrelevant initial state.

The content of item *a* has been known for some time. It is, in fact, subsumed under one of Shannon's famous coding theorems,[6] namely, his noiseless coding theorem (disregarding some technicalities here). This theorem states that conversions among discrete signals are possible typically only by noncausal machines, and, in any case, only if the entropies of input and output are the same.

There is evidently a fairly deep-seated distinction between discrete and continuous signals, and between systems with discrete and continuous-state spaces. It is not known in what kind of questions, other than those discussed here, the distinction matters. It is possible that a connection exists between this phenomenon and one that has been observed in mathematical logic.[7]

AN APPLICATION

I hope to have made a case for our contention that the problem we have posed and its various possible ramifications are of considerable importance in their own rights. Indications are, however, that this problem will apply also to several other fields which might not be immediately associated with it. This notion might be illustrated by outlining the effect it might have on statistical prediction theory.

The object of this theory is to provide methods for the design of causal systems which will accept as input a given random signal, with or without perfectly predictable component, and which will generate as output an extrapolation of the input. This is to say, the output of the system at some time t is a best estimate of what the input will be, for example, at the time $t + 1$. The design of such systems is of no great practical importance in itself. The value of prediction theory lies in the fact that it deals with the simplest problem in the statistical theory of communications and control systems. A successful solution of the prediction problem is, therefore, a logical antecedent to most other problems in this field.

There exists a complete solution to the so-called linear prediction problem. It was arrived at independently by Wiener[7] and Kolmogorov.[3] It applies essentially only to one class of random signals, namely, the Gaussian ones mentioned earlier. In this case, the theory leads to a device which exploits to the hilt the idea of the Wold decomposition. This device, in effect, arrives at its prediction as follows. First, it splits off from the input signal its perfectly predictable component, if any, and extrapolates it. That can be done precisely and without error, owing to the nature of this component.

It remains to extrapolate the information-bearing component of the signal. This, however, cannot be done without error. The predicting device does the best that can be done and proceeds more particularly as follows. The information-bearing component is first converted into white noise. This conversion is always possible. In fact, since Gaussian random signals cannot contain discrete components, it is possible by causal devices. White noise, as we have mentioned above, has the property that all of its samples are statistically independent. In particular, therefore, the unknown future of the white noise is statistically independent of its known past and is useless for purposes of prediction. The device, accordingly, discards it and bases the prediction wholly on the past of the white noise. This, it develops, is not only plausible, but it is, in fact, the best.

It may be noted that, if the hoped for theorem is correct, every one of the steps in this procedure can be executed also with non-Gaussian signals, provided only they contain no discrete component. One can fully expect, therefore, that it will be possible to extend the prediction theory of Wiener and Kolmogorov to a much wider class of random signals than the Gaussian. One can further expect, however, that this theory will not carry over to discrete signals or to signals with discrete components. In fact, indications are that no comparable theory will exist for this case.

Thus, when it comes to prediction theory, there is good reason to hope that our conjectured theorem will permit broad and prompt generalizations. Indications are that the same will be true of filtering theory and at least some portions of control theory. There is, in fact, some reason to hope also that our understanding of communication theory may be enhanced by the exploitation of the consequences of the theorem.

REFERENCES

1. Drenick, R. F., "On the Wold Decomposition of Non-Gaussian Random Processes" (abstract only), *Notices of the Am. Math. Soc.,* **8** (1961), p. 202.
2. Hansen, D. L., "On the Representation Problem for Stationary Stochastic Processes with Trivial Tail Field" (abstract only), *Bull. Am. Math. Soc.,* **68** (1962), p. 115.
3. Kolmogorov, A. N., "Interpolation and Extrapolation of Stationary Random Sequences," *Izv. Akad. Nauk SSSR, Ser. Mat.,* **5** (1941).
4. Levy, Paul, *Théorie de l'addition des variables aleatoires,* Paris (1937).
5. Rosenblatt, M., "Stationary Processes as Shifts of Functions of Independent Variables," *J. Math. Mech.,* **8** (1959), p. 665.
6. Shannon, C. E., and W. Weaver, *The Mathematical Theory of Communication,* University of Illinois Press, Urbana, 1949.
7. Stegmueller, W., *Unvollstaendigkeit und Unentscheidbarkeit,* Vienna 1959.
8. Wiener, N., *Extrapolation and Interpolation of Stationary Time Series,* New York, 1949.
9. Wold, H., *A Study in the Analysis of Stationary Time Series* (Diss), Stockholm (1938).

CHAPTER 12

INTRODUCTORY REMARKS AT PANEL DISCUSSION

W. ROSS ASHBY

What is systems theory? Today the answer is becoming clear, and I would like to describe how the subject seems to be taking form and developing logical coherence.

It dates from about 1940. In that year Howard Aiken completed Mark I and proved to the world that chains of cause and effect, with each effect becoming the next cause, could be extended to an unlimited length. In its length, the trajectory could contain an unlimited quantity of complex processing. At the end of the 1930's, too, the radio engineers succeeded in taming "feedback," so that they could now understand and control unlimited regenerative or circulating cause-and-effect actions. A little later, information theory provided a technique by which large numbers of causes and effects could be counted, even though they were coded into forms that previously had not been recognized as countable. In the 1940's then, the study of systems in which causes and effects acted with great multiplicity rose to an entirely new height.

The study of interacting parts goes back, of course, as far as Newton; and the solution of a set of simultaneous ordinary differential equations,

$$\frac{dx_i}{dt} = f_i(x_1, \cdots, x_n) \qquad i = 1, \cdots, n$$

studies, in some sense exhaustively, the interactions between the n variables x_i. In practice, such equations were manageable only when n was very small, with 5 as a practical maximum, and the theory of big systems with rich interactions tended to be evaded. Science has, in fact, triumphed for 200 years largely because it exploited the many interesting systems in which interaction is small: molecules in a gas at low pressure, so that collisions are rare; crystal structure when the atoms are so little perturbed that the vibrations are almost independent; through the range to neurophysiology, studying reflexes that have only the slightest effect on one another.

Since 1940, however, a serious attempt has been made, aided by the new techniques, to grapple with the problems of the dynamic system that is both large and richly connected internally, so that the effects of interaction are no longer to be ignored, but are, in fact, often the focus of interest. The neurophysiologist no longer deals only with a bundle of unconnected reflexes. The economist wants to consider models which have something like the richness of interaction shown in the real world. The traffic engineer is no longer content to study the case of the crossroads to which cars come only at long intervals!

So has arisen systems theory—the attempt to develop scientific principles to aid us in our struggles with dynamic systems with highly interacting parts.

In "developing scientific principles," however, we must go cautiously. In making use of our heritage of scientific experience, we must take care that we do not unwittingly follow some old rule which is actually obsolete in the new context. I think there is such a danger, which I would like to discuss briefly.

If we study "interactions" generally, and make a preliminary quantitative estimate of what to expect, we often find that the number comes out very large. Then we are apt to characterize it as "astronomical" and to say, "We can't tackle this size just now, but the coming diode is twice as fast, so then we shall be able to do it." I want to suggest that this attitude of mind is seriously in error.

First, what is an "astronomical" number? For example, the time since the earth solidified, in microseconds, is about 10^{23}; the number of atoms in the whole visible universe is about 10^{73}; in fact, all the actual, physically existent astronomical numbers are less than 10^{100}. If we go to the limit, and assume that an atomic event occupies 10^{-10} second, and then ask what is the total number of atomic events that have occurred anywhere in the universe, ever since the earth solidified, we find the number to be about 10^{100}.

In the same spirit, Bremermann[1] has shown that, even if we take single atomic states as markers (i.e., "digits") for computation, the known physical laws make it impossible for any computer made of matter to process more than about 10^{47} bits per gram per second. Let such a computer be as big as the earth and go on for all geological time, it is physically incapable of processing more than about 10^{73} bits. Let me epitomize with:

$$Everything\ material\ stops\ at\ 10^{100}$$

This number is commonly considered large, but we must develop a better sense of proportion in these matters. This number has been obtained by processes that are essentially multiplicative, whereas in systems theory many of our most important quantities grow combinatorially, and this rate is commonly far faster. Here is a simple example that will make the point.

Suppose we have a square block of lamps, for displaying visual patterns, measuring 20 by 20 lamps, and suppose each lamp is either off or on. Obviously there is nothing extravagant about this set of objects. Since each lamp can be off or on, the block can show 2^{400} pictures—about 10^{120}. Suppose now that we are thinking of dividing these pictures into two sets according to some criterion—so that we can say, "This set has the property P, the remainder do not"—from how many properties is the property P picked out? Since each picture may have the property P or not, the number is

$$2^{(10^{120})}$$

As this is $10^{(10^{119.5})}$, we can write it approximately in more convenient form as

$$10^{(10^{120})}$$

How big is this number? To call it "astronomical" is seriously misleading, for the word suggests that it is among the physically achievable numbers, and this is not so. We can get some intuitive grasp of it in the following way:

First notice that $10^{10} - 10^7$ is practically 10^{10}, for it is actually 9,990,000,000. Thus a number 10^K is practically immune to subtraction unless the number subtracted has an exponent within 2 or 3 units of K. Now consider $10^{(10^{80})}$. This number, written out, would be a 1 followed by 10^{80} zeros. As there are only 10^{73} atoms in the universe, there are not enough atoms to carry its zeros; thus $10^{(10^{80})}$ is so large that it cannot be written, in ordinary notation, in our universe.

Finally, what is $10^{(10^{120})} \div 10^{(10^{80})}$? Its exponent is $10^{120} - 10^{80}$, and this (as we saw) is practically 10^{120}. Thus, the number $10^{(10^{120})}$—the number of properties definable on our 20×20 block of lamps—is so large that it is not appreciably affected when divided by a number itself so large that it cannot be written in our universe. This is large indeed!

By comparison with it, the (properly) "astronomical" is hardly distinguishable from the infinitesimal. In particular, the number 10^{100}, given above as the absolute limit to the physically achievable, is now seen to be a restriction of great severity.

What does this mean? It seems to me to have a clear moral. These numbers of *combinatorial* size tend to occur as soon as we start to consider such topics as:

Combinations	Relations
Orderings	Patterns
Subsets	Constraints
Properties	Partitions
Types	Connection-patterns

Every step from the primary set of elements to one of these topics jumps the size to an exponential or factorial function of the original number, and these functions grow far faster than the merely linear or quadratic. To talk, for instance, of *ordering* the *relations* between the *relations* possible on a set jumps the function to something like $(e^{(e^n)})$! If the set is as trivially small as 5—the five types of cloud, for instance—this number is already far beyond the limiting 10^{100}.

Even the elementary question, "I wonder what this machine will do?" carries its sting. If it is of n parts, each of which has only two possible states, its number of states is 2^n. To speculate on its trajectory is to ask (given the initial state) as to which of the $2^n - 1$ will come next; then which of the remaining $2^n - 2$; and so on. The variety we face is of the order of (e^n)!—a function that increases far faster than the exponential, itself often considered explosive!

The systems theorist may thus be defined as a man, with resources not possibly exceeding 10^{100}, who faces problems and processes that go vastly beyond this size. What is he to do?

At this point, it seems to me, he must make up his mind whether to accept this limit or not. If he does not, let him attack it and attempt to find a way of defeating it. If he does accept it, let him accept it wholeheartedly and consistently. My own opinion is that this limit is much less likely to yield than, say, the law of conservation of energy. The energy law is essentially empirical, and may vanish overnight, as the law of conservation of mass did, but the restriction that prevents a man with resources of 10^{100} from carrying out a process that genuinely calls for more than this quantity rests on our basic ways of thinking about cause and effect, and is entirely independent of the particular material on which it shows itself.

If this view is right, systems theory must become based on methods of simplification, and will be founded, essentially, on the *science* of simplification. Many sciences, of course, have used simplifications, and R. A. Fisher [2] said, without qualification, ". . . the object of statistical methods is the reduction of data." But simplifications today are often used apologetically because of the fear that it will be called an "over"-simplification, though when a simplification becomes an "over"-simplification is often clear to no one.

The science of simplification has, I think, been well started by the mathematicians in their studies of homomorphisms, but much remains to be done, and many questions essential for applications have to be answered. For example: Is every act of simplification, as it occurs in the daily work of the scientist, *always* an application of an equivalence relation over the primary set, or are there other methods? Does Bourbaki's [3] formulation of a property being "compatible" (with an equivalence relation) correspond always to "this is not an over-simplification"? Can the methods of simplification be classified and studied systematically? (here we remember, of course, that the "ways of grouping" are themselves apt to increase with combinatorial speed). The science of simplification clearly has its own techniques and its own sophistication. The systems theorist of the future, I suggest, must be an expert in how to simplify.

REFERENCES

1. Bremermann, H. J., "Optimization Through Evolution and Re-combination," in *Self-Organizing Systems* (Yovits, M. C., Jacobi, G. T., and Goldstein, G. D., eds.), Spartan Books, Washington, D. C., 1962.
2. Fisher, R. A., "On the Mathematical Foundations of Theoretical Statistics," *Phil. Trans. Roy. Soc. Lond.*, A, **222** (1922), pp. 309–368.
3. Bourbaki, N., *Théorie des ensembles; fascicule de résultats*, ASEI 1141, Hermann & Cie., Paris, 1958 (3rd edition).

CHAPTER 13

REMARKS ON GENERAL SYSTEMS THEORY

ANATOL RAPOPORT

Russell Ackoff's remarks on general systems theory and systems research raise some important methodological issues. I believe, however, that these issues can be raised without posing questions which cannot be meaningfully answered, such as which will "succeed" in unifying science, this or that approach. No approach and no program devised by mortals will succeed in "unifying science" any more than any social or economic arrangements will "unify mankind." But just as some social, political, and economic arrangements contribute more to the resolution of conflicts among men than do others, so certain methodologies contribute more to integrating knowledge than others. For example, we are now aware that a catalog of facts, such as Francis Bacon envisaged, would be a sterile approach from the point of view of integrating knowledge, because the next step, "generalizations derived from juxtaposition of facts," would not be fruitful unless some conceptual theoretical scheme guided the generalizations and, incidentally, the selection of facts to be recorded.

Actually, every theoretical scheme is a step toward integrating facts into an *area* of knowledge, and so even the conventional "disciplines" are schemes of unification. Ackoff is right in criticizing a purely formal extension of this process ("now that we have unified facts into areas of knowledge and created disciplines, let us unify the disciplines"). This unimaginative procedure has resulted in many abortive ventures, but I do not think that general systems theorists have ever advocated such schemes. They are traceable to administrative rather than scientific ideas.

To the extent that general systems theorists have made sanguine prognoses of "unifying science," they may have been guilty of utopian dreaming. But to the extent that concrete steps of conceptual unification have been proposed, they have made a number of significant contributions. In particular, Bertalanffy's *specific* contribution, I believe, has been in calling attention to the dynamic equilibrium properties of open systems and to their resemblance to some aspects of the living process. He was one of the earliest thinkers to point this out. Much work has been done since then on the thermodynamics of irreversible processes and the importance of these processes in biology has become apparent.

R. W. Gerard has extended the insights of grand-scale biology to a conceptualization of systems. It is a long way from a "conceptualization" to concrete theoretical results, but neither are such results obtained in a conceptual vacuum. The connection between a conceptual scheme and a fruitful line of concrete investigation is not usually apparent, but it is the job of a philosopher, especially a philosopher of science, to discern these connections. Their importance is not to be discounted.

Emphasis of mathematical isomorphisms also stems from general systems theory. The theoretical import of these isomorphisms has been greatly misunderstood; nor do the comments by Jonas, Hempel and Bertalanffy, quoted by Ackoff in Chapter 4, really clarify the issue. This is a big subject, and I can only suggest to interested people to refer to the voluminous literature on it. I will confine myself to a single example. The isomorphism of Heisenberg's matrix approach to quantum mechanics and Schroedinger's wave equation approach is not something to which one should say, "So what?" Some isomorphisms may seem trivial, but some are profoundly insightful. And even those which appear trivial today, like the ones cited by Hempel and Bertalanffy, were once anything but obvious. The drawing of mathematical isomorphisms is of prime importance in welding disparate content areas into single, structural-theoretic schemes.

Of all the issues raised by Ackoff, I agree most heartily with his conception of science as an activity rather than as a body of facts, laws, and theories. To quote Henry Margenau, "All of man's facts have become acts." But now what is an "activity"? No doubt some "problem" is always involved in an activity, but what is a real "problem"? Do all problems necessarily arise from some "practical" concern, such as a notion of designing an efficient inventory policy? Admittedly, these concerns have spurred on the sort of activity that resulted in what we call science. In the old days, those were the problems of navigation and ballistics, later the problems of converting one form of energy into another, and of combating disease, and still later the problems of organizing large collective efforts, the area to which operations research most directly applies. But how about Descartes, lying sick in bed and watching the motion of a point on a tree framed by the window pane? Was he not engaging in an "activity" and was not its result the unification of algebra and geometry (the first "hybrid discipline")?

I see well the distinction between involvement in an honest-to-god problem and sterile formalistic systematization. I do not believe the distinction has to do with that between concrete "real life" problems and abstract problems of conceptualization. The distinction has to do with whether the investigator has a problem at all. What makes the formalistically oriented systematizer sterile is that he really has no problem at all. He already has the answers, and his "activity" amounts to little more than boring with his "answers" people who are involved with real, painful problems.

Now anyone can be a bore, whether his "answer" is reductionism, or general systems theory, or dialectical materialism, or technocracy (which is the dogmatic perversion of the ideas that inspire operations research). It is equally true that fertile ideas, conceptualizations, and theories come, sometimes quite unexpectedly, from people of all philosophical persuasions.

CHAPTER 14

AN APPROACH TO GENERAL SYSTEMS THEORY

C. WEST CHURCHMAN

I should like to present an axiomatic approach to general systems theory. I do not pretend that this approach is universally acceptable to all those interested in the topic, nor do I claim that the axioms presented below are self-evident, except in Ambrose Bierce's sense that they are evident only to myself.

However, I expect that those interested in general systems theory will want to display as many approaches as possible to the topic, lest this exciting intellectual effort generate an insignificant closed group of frustrated academics.

The intent of the axioms is to state two things: (1) that systems are complexes that can be designed and evaluated, and (2) that the adjective "general" in the phrase "general systems theory" modifies "systems" as well as "theory." The axioms are as follows:

1. *Systems are designed and developed.* A necessary condition for design is the ability to evaluate. Hence, systems can be evaluated, and alternative systems can be proposed which can be judged to be better or worse than the original. If one goes at the matter more precisely, it is possible to set up an objective function for alternative systems subject to a set of constraints which themselves represent certain types of desired goals on the part of the systems designer.

"Development" includes the implementation of the system design and the changes of the design in the light of continued experience.

It goes without saying that this meaning of systems excludes astronomical systems, mechanical systems, and the like, unless these systems are conceived, as Professor Mesarovic states, as sets of assertions. In this case, the systems are designed to describe events, and such systems comply with the first axiom, since they can be both designed and developed.

2. *Systems are component-designed.* The designer conceives of

a design as consisting of a set of subproblems, the solution to each subproblem leading to a component of the larger system.

3. *The components of systems are also systems.* This means that each component can be evaluated and developed in the sense described above. It also means that each component can be conceived as having subcomponents, and that there is no logical end to this process, although the designer, in practice, will choose to stop the process and regard the last components as "simple building blocks."

4. *A system is* closed *if its evaluation does not depend on the design of its environment within a specific class of environments.* The meaning of this axiom is that the designer attempts to attain a stable system which will retain its value even though the environment changes. Whenever the designer feels that probable environmental changes may bring about unsatisfactory performance in the system, he tries to enlarge the system design to take care of these environmental jolts. When he thinks that he has gone far enough in this process, he regards the system as closed. Usually the designer does not attempt to account for all possible environmental changes. If he does, then we have the following:

5. *A general system is a system that is closed and remains closed for all possible environments.* That is, a general system represents ultimate stability with respect to environmental change.

The questions one can raise about general systems remind us of issues familiar to traditional philosophy. First of all, how many members are there in the class of general systems? If the answer is "none," then we have philosophical anarchism. If the answer is "one," we have philosophical monism, as expressed, say, by the Stoics, Spinoza, Leibniz, etc. If the answer is "many," we have philosophical pluralism. Second, there is the question of whether a general system is good. In general, I think it should be made clear by systems designers that it is easily possible to design systems for evil as well as good. No very useful purpose is served by trying to distinguish between design functions which meet scientific criteria of excellence and design functions concerned with the evil and good of systems. The systems designer has equal responsibility to apply the best knowledge and technology available as well as satisfactory criteria of ethical performance. Nevertheless, one might want to argue that, if man ever succeeds in generating a generally closed system, the result will be an evil system rather than a good one. For example, the only possible closed system may be the total destruction of the human spirit. The following two axioms summarize my beliefs on these issues:

6. *There exists one and only one general system (monism).*

7. *The general system is optimal* (*optimism*).

The most general task of system design is to approximate a general system. That is:

8. *General system theory is the methodology of searching for the general system.*

One concluding axiom that few will feel inclined to deny:

9. *The search becomes more difficult with time and is never completed* (*realism*).

INDEX